£14.99

C000026273

Acknowledgements

Richard Dale and Colin Cameron would like to thank a number of people for their help in the writing of the **contenders**: Peter Georgi for coming up with the concept and the title, for taking many of the photographs and for working so hard for over a year on the project; Ben Hamilton, Helen Thomas and Andrew Thompson who worked with Peter on the television series and whose research was invaluable for the book; Peter Allden from the BBC Sports Department for putting together the "main contenders" sections; Jake Lingwood at Boxtree; Adrian Smith, Nigel Meakin and Chris Hartley, three of the BBC's finest cameramen, for their exceptional photography; Irna Farrah Imran and Lucy Oliver for all their invaluable help, particularly with the typing; Sanjida O'Connell for all her useful comments; and finally, Dorothy Prior, Unit Manager on the TV series, without whom neither the films nor the book could ever have been produced.

Above all, we would like to thank the contenders themselves: Zita Lusack, Shirley McIntosh, Stephen Ward, Richard Nerurkar, Martin Steele, Marvin Campbell, Neil Thomas, Jo Wright, Nick Ponting, Gill Clarke, Chris Hunt, the Scottish wrestling squad, the Scottish Women's Bowls team, Ian Wilson, Nlck Gillingham, Kerry Shacklock, Debbie Southwick, Robert Morgan, Matthew Yates, Yvonne Murray, Sally Gunnell, Linford Christie, Mike Edwards, Colin Jackson, Steve Backley, Graeme Obree, Chris Boardman, Kelly Holmes, Darren Campbell, Danny Williams and Megan Still. The best of luck to them all.

A glossy *BBC Contenders Magazine,* packed with educational information about the series is available from:

BBC Education
201 Wood Lane
London   W12 7TS

the contenders

RICHARD DALE

AND

COLIN CAMERON

BOXTREE

First Published in the UK in 1994 by
Boxtree Limited
21 Broadwall
London SE1 9PL

10987654321

Design by Design 23
Jacket design by Hammond Hammond
Printed and bound in Great Britain by
Bath Press Colourbooks, Glasgow

A CIP catalogue for this book is available from the British Library

ISBN: 0 7522 0948 5

Photograph Acknowledgements

Kenny Cowburn, food shots pages 74-75
Andrew Thompson, pages 44-45
Peter Lane, pages 11, 26, 92, 97
Stuart Sadd, page 77
Evonne Francis, back flap
All other photographs were taken by the copyright holders, above

CONTENTS

FOREWORD 7

THE CONTENDERS – THE BOOK 9

THE HUMAN MACHINE 21

THE FUTURE'S IN THE FRIDGE 51

TOOLS OF THE TRADE 83

MIND GAMES 109

CHARIOTS OF FIRE 133

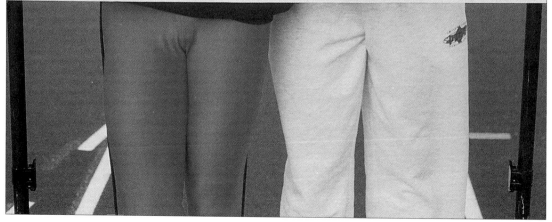

the **contenders**

FOREWORD

"There is always something more you can learn. Accept that, and you are on your way to being a champion."

Colin Jackson and Linford Christie

Scientists tend to generalise. They say, "This is what we think and this is what you all should do". Very often that is far from the truth.

There are no universal answers, no 'Right Ways' to win. There are only things that are right for individuals. But that means there is something out there for everyone, something that is right for you. You must believe in yourself. You should never be content with just taking part. Always do the best you can.

But you must never believe that you know too much. We are all our own sports scientists in a way. We have got to experiment, we have got to listen and try new ideas. You can always learn, even from people who are not as good as you. No matter how long you have been doing a sport, any kind of sport, there is always something more you can learn.

Accept that, and you are on your way to being a champion.

Linford Christie

Colin Jackson

Colin Jackson and Linford Christie wearing head-cams developed to give TV audiences a Contender's point of view.

THE CONTENDERS
–THE BOOK

"You don't understand... I could've been a contender,
I could've been somebody."
Terry Malloy (Marlon Brando) – On the Waterfront, Columbia Pictures

I was lucky enough to be at the 1993 Athletics Grand Prix final at Crystal Palace. It was the first athletics meeting I had ever been to and the atmosphere was electrifying. But one moment sticks in my mind. It was after the men's 400 metre final. Eight of the world's finest athletes had lined up and, like gladiators, pitted themselves against each other in front of a crowd of thousands. At the end of the race all the cameras and the commentators followed the winner as he paraded around the track on a lap of honour.

But on the finish line behind him were seven of the finest athletes in the world who had lost. Each was walking as if in a trance, completely isolated, heading back down 100 metres of plain red track to the exit from the arena, to their locker rooms and to confront the reality that they had failed. Could they hear the crowd? Were they aware of each other? What would they go and do now? A commentator would ask the breathless winner "How does it feel?" and get an adrenaline filled platitude, but who was going to ask these other questions?

There has never been a documentary series on sports people.

Though many sportsmen and women are household names and, one might imagine, ideal fodder for televised scrutiny, and though the activities they perform are, in almost all cases, highly visual, somehow they have slipped though the film-makers net. What has made programme makers blind to the wealth of real-life drama in the lives of the world's best athletes? After all, it would not be too uncharitable to say that documentary makers are usually only too happy to make programmes on anything that moves, let alone things that move as beautifully as a diver, or a hurdler.

Is it because there is nothing interesting to say about sports people? Is it because, as

Robert Morgan, high-board diver. Diving from a height of 10 metres he enters the water at over 30mph.

contemporary heroes, they are above examination? Or is it because both film-makers and the public have no idea that there is anything more to being a top athlete than coming out onto a track and running a little?

When we were first given the opportunity to look into this area, the realisation that we were in largely uncharted territory was fantastic. Sport is filled with engaging and emotional stories from people with status akin to pop stars, and with fascinating nuggets of behind-the-scenes information. Furthermore, there are opportunities to capture images that no one has ever seen before.

We were also in a unique position. Unlike conventional sports programmes on television, we were not constrained to show a result: we did not need to have a wide shot of the 100 metre race because we were not interested in who came second. We did not need to show both boxers in the ring as we were not having to score the fight. Instead we were free to show sport from a different angle: the faces before competition, the tense, quiet warm-up; the hard, dirty, noisy punches, the real struggles that are going on. We could develop new techniques to film the finest sports people of our time and show the beauty and power of the human body as never before.

Between the covers of this book, along with interviews and behind-the-scenes glimpses into the lives of the world's sporting elite, we have tried to give an account of how we set about doing this. Original strips of film from the programmes have been reproduced in full colour and, at the end of each chapter, there is a section that tells of the filming process itself: what we set out to do, why we set out to do it and what went wrong when we tried!

As well as bringing a new perspective to sports imagery, the unique relationship we established with our contenders enabled us to get beyond the facade many have erected to shield themselves from the media probing that high-profile individuals invariably receive. Many of the pictures and intimate interviews in this book are a tribute to that trust.

In making the television series, we aimed not only at sports fans and science enthusiasts, but at anyone who is interested in people. Sportsmen and women are undoubtedly special - special because they do things to the extreme, special because they are the best - but mostly because they are just people. We all have a certain level of commitment, of skill, and of determination; they simply have a higher one. They are human beings just like you and I, *only more so*. This book follows that philosophy: it is about people.

When we first set out to explore the area of sport science we expected that we would do so by looking at each sport and its science separately, or perhaps by considering one scientific discipline at a time - a chapter on biochemistry, one on physiology and so on. But very soon we realised this would be a mistake. The reason is simple: there is no such thing as "Sports Science".

We had expected that we would find researchers and theoreticians plotting and planning on every final straight on every track where a world champion had ever pressed an expensively shod foot. But whereas some sports people, like Olympic pursuit cycling gold medallist Chris Boardman, or World indoor 3000m champion Yvonne Murray, do have highly technical and expert scientific back-up, for others "Sports Science" means simply "whatever

The making of The Contenders required the development of ground-breaking filming techniques. Here Robert Morgan is captured mid-flight.

I do". Linford Christie put it best to us. "We are all our own sports scientists" he said. "We all need to keep learning, when we stop doing that we die."

Because our investigation had to be a true reflection of the world of top class sportsmen and women, had to be faithful to them and to their aspirations, we threw away our preconceived notions. We decided that our approach would be to make an account not of science in sport but of *people* in sport: Each chapter would concentrate on a different aspect of sportsmen and women's build-up to competition, from long term training and diet, through to equipment design and on-the-blocks mental techniques. And through their struggle to achieve their best we would see the impact of science and technology on their life. And it would not be just 'science and technology' as people reading "Hi-Fi Enthusiast" would understand, but real, living, useful knowledge that shapes and affects sports people's lives.

Whilst this is the only truly meaningful approach to take on the subject, it does throw up something of a problem for those wishing to distil a scientific text for athletic achievement. Namely that the number of theories you can find on how to achieve top-flight sporting success is exactly equal to the number of top-flight sports people you are prepared to ask. And furthermore, the conviction with which each top-flight sports person will argue for their own theory is directly proportional to how "top" their "top-flight" position is.

Martin Steele, for instance, puts his recent success, clocking the second fastest time in the world for 800 metres in 1993, down to the fact that his new coach has organised his training diary around his biorhythm chart, and furthermore, that he is bound to be successful because he was born within a fortnight of Steve Ovett and Sebastian Coe.

To someone like Yvonne Murray and her coach, who rely on the scientifically orthodox to plan their training regime, this would sound frankly barmy. But, at the top level of sport, where races are won or lost by fractions of fractions of seconds, what is perhaps more important than having a theory which is "right" according to a scientist in a laboratory, is having a theory which you *believe* is right.

Great Britain's Neil Thomas, mid-way through his floor routine. The speed of gymnastics at top international levels means that complex manoeuvres must be accomplished unconsciously.

If one were looking to coin a scientific-sounding term to describe the phenomenon, it could be the "Deaf Spider Syndrome", after the fictitious spider which was trained by a researcher to respond to spoken commands: move left, move right, somersault, and so on. When it could perform the tasks repeatedly, the researcher pulled off its legs and tried giving the commands again: move left! Unsurprisingly, the spider did not respond very well, so the researcher came closer and shouted very loudly. But still the spider did not move. Of course, being an intelligent man, the researcher reached the obvious conclusion that when he had pulled the spider's legs off, it had gone deaf.

The point is, it is the result that matters: whether the researcher believes the spider is deaf or not, it still will not move. Likewise if Martin Steele believes it is biorhythms that have turned him from a club runner into an international contender, why argue? After all, he was the fastest man in Great Britain over 800m last year. Besides that, he might even be right! Is anyone really sure spiders don't go deaf when you pull their legs off?

So where does this leave us in our quest for the axioms of sporting achievement? Is sports science all simply an elaborate psychological game? If everyone has a different theory *are* there no hard and fast rules, no scientific secrets to success? The answer is, of course, No... And Yes.

No, there are no rules, because it is never possible in a field where so much depends on individual effort, to separate the effects of the mind from those of the body. If two identical people line up against each other, both having trained physically to exactly the same degree, the chances are that the one who believes she has the better system will win.

And Yes, there are rules, because beneath the superficially different theories patterns do emerge: both Yvonne Murray's scientific scheduling and Martin Steele's astrological plots mean that they train less than they might otherwise do, reflecting a definite shift in all top level successful sports towards quality work rather than quantity, giving the body time to recover fully from hard training sessions: building up strength rather than limb-numbing tiredness.

What the myriad different opinions passionately held by different champions show is not the lack of consensus in sporting circles, but that at the top levels of sport, belief (and more specifically *self* belief) is at least as important as science.

As a consequence of this tension, every aspect of sportsmen and women's lives are filled with conundrums and contradictions. In this book you will read the views of different world champions on the whole gamut of sporting life, from diet through to the nurturing of talent in future generations. Often one champion's perspective will be diametrically opposed to another's, but the joy in sharing their thoughts is in deciphering the patterns beneath them. It is behind the rhetoric of self-confidence (blustering or sincerely felt) that the true scientific keys to success, the general rules of international achievement, can occasionally be glimpsed. They are fairly simple notions, but their simplicity belies their importance.

In chapter one, The Human Machine, the subject explored is training, and the scientific golden-rule is when not to.

Everyone has a body with fundamental limitations: a heart that can only pump so much, lungs that will only grow so big. Whereas an accident of birth can give you an advantage, that alone isn't enough: winners may be born but they are not born winning.

The key to success lies in making the most of the genetic lucky-dip and maximising the body's potential. Traditionally you get three choices: train hard, train hard or train harder. Today, science is showing another way. Peter Keen, Chris Boardman's coach and a lecturer in sports physiology at Brighton University, has put it this way:

"Nature has given the human body a wonderful engine management system. It actually responds to stress by adapting to cope with it better...

It's like driving a car so hard that it packs in, leaving it overnight and then finding that it runs even better in the morning."

The bottom line is that the body does not get fitter through exercise, it gets fitter through *recovering* from exercise. This has a fundamental impact on an athlete's training regime: they must give their bodies time to recover. In other words, they must know when *not* to train. To anyone who spends their life not training, it sounds rather easy, but as World Champion pursuit cyclist Graeme Obree said to us, "The hardest thing for an athlete to do is not to train. You can't sit still, you feel you should be out there working."

Once you understand this obsession with training and the all consuming guilt that accompanies abstinence, the various odd and often rather 'unscientific' methods athletes employ in order to help them rest become understandable. It is possible to see them as means to the same simple end - to achieve more by doing less. In the watchwords of the scientifically up-to-date coach, Quality not Quantity.

The other scientific lesson underscoring the modern contenders' training techniques is also unnervingly simple. In one word, specificity: teaching your body in training to do what it will have to do in competition. Traditionally, training diaries have been filled with a whole range of exercises for the budding sports star which have little or no relationship to their chosen event. Increasingly, the rationale behind their inclusion is being questioned. Again Graeme Obree puts it delightfully clearly:

"My event lasts four and a half minutes on the cycle track. A traditional coach might tell me to train a hundred miles a day to build up stamina. That's rubbish.

I need to train at going as fast as I can for four and a half minutes. All that cycling one hundred miles a day would make me good at is cycling one hundred miles a day."

Obree's disarming logic is, perhaps surprisingly, at the cutting edge of athletic thinking. Throughout the sporting world, tradition has not only a firm grip, but very often a stranglehold on reason.

There are cases, however, where tradition has fluked it scientifically. Perhaps the finest example of this as regards specificity in training is gymnastics.

From the very beginning of a gymnast's career, the training they do is geared exclusively to performing the tasks they will eventually accomplish on the apparatus. Though upper body strength is a must for the crucifix position on rings, for instance, you will never find a gymnast pumping-iron. In fact, you will never find weights in a gymnast's training arena.

You will, however, find a range of outlandish training devices including, at the gym where two of Great Britain's top performers train in Liverpool, a plastic bucket on a rope. The reason for the bucket is simple: if the best way to train for an exercise is to perform the exercise, one must find a way of enabling gymnasts who are not yet able to perform the exercise to do so. Only then will their muscles 'learn' what it feels like and, eventually, be able to carry the gymnast unsupported. The bucket is one of these techniques. As Marvin

Medal-winning Marvin Campbell. His performances on the pommel horse are aided in training by nothing more than a household bucket.

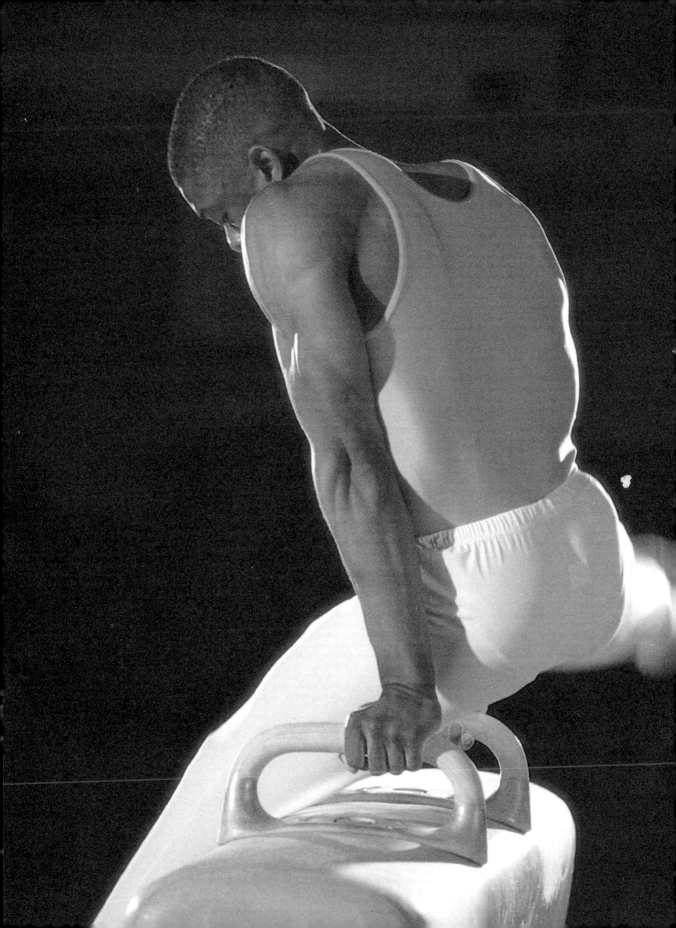

Campbell, 1993 English Artistic Gymnastic Champion puts it, "The bucket is simply a way of taking some of my weight. I put my feet in the bucket and I can revolve slowly around the pommels, I can do a World Championship routine up here like this again and again."

Chapter two, The Future's in the Fridge, deals with diet and, as any sports scientist will tell you, there are three things to remember. Diet is the most active area of sports based scientific research, it is the area where the right knowledge can bring the biggest sporting gains, and it is the hardest thing in the world to get an athlete to change.

For *diet* read *lifestyle*:- steak and eggs before the fight, not eating during a race, pasta for supper on the night before. For athletes, food can have as much to do with their mind as with their bodies. But as advances in physiology reveal more about the demands sports make on the body, more and more sports people are fighting against their own traditions and looking towards changes in diet as a way of achieving their best.

The area where diet can have the most impact is in endurance events. For Chris Boardman, making the transition from short track races to challenges like the three week Tour de France, performance is a delicate balancing act of diet and fitness.

The Future's in the Fridge also looks at the point where "diet" becomes "food supplement" and where that food supplement might one day, according to the whim (or, rather, to the scientifically derived conclusion) of the governing authorities, become an illegal drug.

For athletes, the fine line between illegal substance and permitted supplement is simple. As Colin Jackson says of his chosen additive, the energy enhancing Creatine, "The difference between Creatine and a drug like Anabolic Steroids is simple: one is on the banned list, the other is not." This does not illustrate that the finest sprint hurdler of all time is taking something he shouldn't. Creatine naturally occurs in red meat and Jackson merely takes it in concentrated form. Neither is he ignorant of the vast difference between the medical effects of the two as it is well known that steroids are dangerous when misused. The point he is making is that the only criterion of significance to an athlete who is convinced that taking a certain substance will help them win is, "*is it legal or not?*"

To the public, obsessed with moral issues, the very black-and-whiteness of this supposed grey-area may come as something of a surprise.

Tools of the Trade, chapter three, looks at how technology shapes sport. From highly visible equipment innovations to barely noticeable back-stage gadgetry - technological advances shift the goal-posts of international competition. For athletes who stay one step ahead, technological changes can be the key to success, but the race never stops, and we might not like the place that it is heading.

In the chapter, four stories illustrate the different ways in which technical innovation can affect a sports person's life. Bobby Morgan could possibly elevate himself to world number one thanks to high-speed computer analysis of his dives by a team from Leeds University. Chris Boardman, the champion of new bike designs, confronts the realisation that, once you start the innovation ball rolling, you have to be prepared to keep on running with it. He faces a challenge, both technologically and athletically, from the maverick Scot, Graeme Obree.

Steve Backley tells of the runaway advances in javelin construction that, until the authorities stepped in, made his event more like a testing ground for aeronautical engineers that a field of combat for the modern day athletic warrior. And a top coach reflects on the forces that today make women's gymnastics not a sport for women at all, but one so technically demanding it is suitable only for the bodies of pre-pubescent girls.

The most colourful and contradictory of the arenas where science impacts on the lives of the sporting elite comes under scrutiny in Mind Games, the fourth chapter.

Top athletes need three things: physical ability, mental determination and the resilience to use them both in extreme measures. Champions need something more.

At the very top, what separates a winner from an 'also ran' is in their head.

A champion needs a conviction that, above all else, only one person will win... And it will be them.

Some athletes insist they need no help in building this supreme confidence: Linford Christie, for instance, gives sports psychology and its practitioners short shrift. He, like the less flamboyant champion Nick Gillingham, World 200m breaststroke winner, takes pride in his ability to motivate and mentally prepare himself alone. For others, the task of forging their egos into an unassailable fortress of self belief is only manageable with the expert help of the sports scientist.

The English badminton squad get specialist psychological assistance from Tom Fawcett, a wily scouser whose chief task is to help them combine phenomenal individual power and skill into useful doubles combinations. The difficulty for both Fawcett and the players is that badminton is, for the most part, a game for individuals. Assets such as teamwork and co-operation, so vital for the doubles and mixed doubles, are normally completely irrelevant.

Graeme Obree. 'I need to train at going as fast as I can for four-and-a-half minutes. All that cycling one hundred miles a day would make me good at is cycling one hundred miles a day.'

Getting players to acknowledge their own strengths and weaknesses, as well as those of their partner, so that they can dovetail into an effective team is a great challenge.

Building a team psychology is also the task of Dr Richard Cox, psychologist to the Scottish Ladies' Bowls team. Whilst bowls is not traditionally a sport where science has exercised a significant influence, Cox, with his carefully planned psychological input has been instrumental in changing the very level of the competition. He has worked with the team on techniques that allow them to take full mental control of the game, from simple things like not being afraid to shout encouragement to each other, to the delightfully subtle: he tells them never to stand with folded arms, which looks suppressed and sulky, but always with hand on hips and feet challengingly apart.

Cox claims they never do anything outside the rules of the game but he does admit to taking every advantage they permit. Just how far this gamesmanship goes he is reluctant to say, but the team themselves point out with some pride that they are not the Scottish Ladies' team, but the Scottish *Women's* one! Whatever they call themselves, one thing is certain: they are the World Champions in three of the five recognised bowls categories (triples, fours and team) and confidently predict taking at least one Commonwealth gold medal.

Chapter five, Chariots of Fire, takes a broader look at the world of the contenders. It asks whether the days of the medal-winning amateur are gone for good. The question is as much practical as it is philosophical because it impacts greatly on the lives of today's and tomorrow's contenders.

In Australia the government has established an Institute of Sport, a centre of excellence, to use the parlance of modern management, devoted to the identification and development of future champions. Their philosophy, convincingly stated by director Rob de Castella, is "To apply science, technology and modern management techniques to the business of sport. And by doing so, to win medals."

It seems to work: Australia has moved steadily up the medal winning league since the inception of the institute in the early 1980s and they feel confident enough to set themselves a target of 60 medals at the Olympics in 2000 - a tally that will put them 5th in the order of merit. It is a formidable target, even with the home advantage, and it speaks loudly of their national commitment to International sporting excellence.

By contrast, Great Britain relies on the efforts of the individual, many of whom feel they succeed *despite* the national sporting organisations rather than *because* of them. Malcolm Arnold, coach to many up and coming elite athletes as well as to Colin Jackson, puts it thus: "Great Britain gets more from her athletes than she deserves. We put nothing in, yet expect everything out."

Which system is best? Is there something disturbing about a country which intends to screen every 11 to 15 year old schoolchild to identify those with physical attributes that might in six years time make them a national hero? Does the calculation of money-in verses medals-out ignore the personal element and offend traditional "gentlemanly" sensibilities? And does any of that matter: can we afford to muse on morality whilst Great Britain is

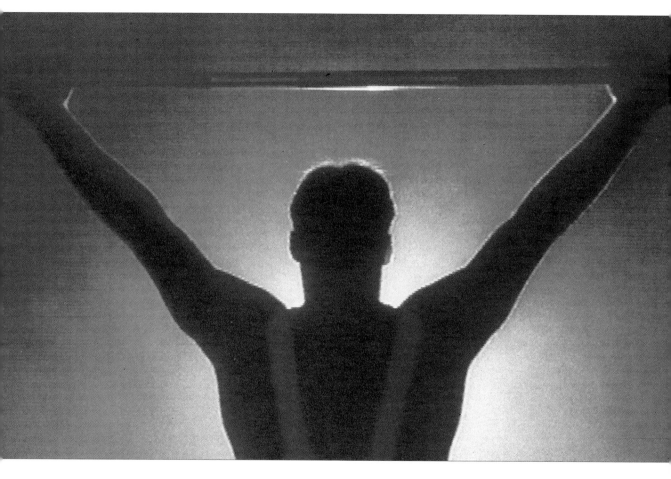

slipping down the medal tables, our elite athletes are forced to quit through lack of resources, and other countries pass us by?

This book gives the athletes' answers to those questions. It is the result of filming some of the world's finest sportsmen and women over the course of a year and of analysing their thoughts on every aspect of how science and technology touches their lives.

The unique interviews that form the spine of each chapter contain revelations about their training, anxieties and secret aspirations, as well as giving some inspiring insights into human souls pushed to the limits of endurance.

The book provides an inside view into the making of a TV series and shows sports stars usually only pictured on the winners' rostrum or at stagy photo-calls documented in *real life*.

Enjoy it.

Only total belief in their ability will enable weightlifters like Steven Ward to improve their personal best. Each lift is heavier than anything they have ever lifted before.

THE HUMAN MACHINE

"If you want to be a champion,
you've got to train like a contender."
Linford Christie, Commonwealth, Olympic and World 100m champion.

Anyone can be an athlete. It's just that some are faster, stronger, more powerful - BETTER AT IT - than others.

Linford Christie is better. Indeed, he was the best throughout 1993, a year in which he became World champion in the 100 metres. It was confirmation of his global superiority; the previous year he became Olympic champion. Linford Christie, "The Fastest Man in the World": it is the only appropriate description for Britain's premier athlete.

Christie has achieved his success by maximising his potential. As a young man, he was less dedicated than some of his rivals but still managed to beat them through sheer natural ability. But he was a long way short of running as fast as his body was capable of. Without a commitment to training, Christie was fast, but not the fastest; great, but not the greatest. In order to achieve what he has achieved, he had to train. And train hard.

Q. Do you enjoy training?
LINFORD CHRISTIE: If I didn't enjoy training, I wouldn't do it. Training is fun, it's the time when you try all different things.

Does it make you run faster?
No, training doesn't make you run faster, because when you get to the race you've got adrenalin pumping, you've got everything going, so that makes you go that much quicker. When you're training, you should always train with the thought in mind that you can go at least ten per cent faster. If you run flat out in your training, then that's as fast as you're ever going to get.

Linford Christie sets a new European and Commonwealth 100m record of 9.87 seconds at the 1993 World Championships in Stuttgart.

You seem very determined in your training?

I never drop. My motto is "Always train like the contender". You see, I train like the guy down there who wants to get where I am. I don't want to get complacent, so I train as if I'm not a champion. I still want to be a champion, which is what it's all about. If you train like a champion you say "Oh, but I'm there," and you get complacent. I train like a contender, never like a champion. That's what it's all about. You see, because these guys want to have what I've got, they want to be where I am, they're going to train that much harder. They've got a target. I haven't got a target, so I've got to make a target. I have to put myself in their position and think, if I wanted to be world champion how would I train? And I train exactly the same as them, but only ten per cent more.

How does the training work with you and your coach, Ron Roddan?

Over the years, I realised that I needed to train. I don't train because Ron wants me to train, I train because I like to train and I know I need to. Ron works out my track sessions and I'm just doing what he tells me. You build up a trust and it just goes on from there. If he tells me to do something, I do it. Sometimes I question, obviously because I need him to explain to me why I'm doing certain things and, if I don't agree, I tell him and we work things out together. There are times when I see something new that I'd like to do and I tell him and we'll discuss it before I do it. He can see things that I can't see and I think he knows me as well as I know myself.

Trainer Ron Roddan had to tell Christie some uncomfortable truths in order to spur him on to greater things.

■ Christie trains with Roddan, a fixture throughout his rise to prominence and ultimate ascendancy to supremacy. It was Roddan who confronted Christie with the reality that he was an under-achiever, someone who was dabbling in athletics. He told him (in as many words!) that it wasn't worth running if he did not commit himself fully to maximising his potential, that inferior athletes would beat him through their determination. Christie, a proud man, was moved. And he was scared. Scared that he would grow old without the respect of his fellow athletes. Respect is Christie's motivation. Roddan's comments struck deep into the heart of the athlete's complex personality.

Christie takes his responsibility as a role model very seriously; he never refuses a request for an autograph.

All this was a long time ago. It followed Christie's failure to earn selection for the 1984 Olympic Games. Now, such an oversight is unthinkable. Christie is the captain of Great Britain's athletics team, an automatic choice, a leader, someone whom young athletes consider a role model.

Achieving this transformation required hours of training, specific to Christie's physique and goals. The best modern athletes have schedules that have been tailored to suit themselves and their events' requirements. The 100 metres is a controlled event won by the man who runs the best race, not the person who can run fastest. There are three distinct sections, the start and first 30 metres, the next 30 metres at full stride and the remaining 40 metres where athletes hang on to top speed as long as possible. Christie's programme is geared towards improving specific aspects of his running so that the sum parts are a winning whole.

Basic fitness is the minimum requirement. (It hedges against races being lost through failure to maintain speed to the line). Real success is founded in sustaining excellence throughout the race, beginning with the start.

Christie has struggled in the past to perfect his start. A tall man, it can take time for him to unfold his limbs and get into his stride. Roddan was not happy with Christie's speed out of the blocks at the Tokyo World Championships in 1989 and they worked on it, shortening his first few steps. It was not perfect by the Barcelona Olympics in 1992, but it was good enough to win gold. It still has faults and is a part of Christie's discipline that he can improve on, so he has trained specifically with the goal of a perfect start as the target. ▶

Q. As you're pretty tall, do you suffer a significant disadvantage at the start? How does that affect you?
LINFORD CHRISTIE: It's a disadvantage as much as you want it to be a disadvantage. It's not about the start, it's about the finishing. A 60 metre race for me is fairly short, but I hold the British and European record for that so there's not that much wrong with my starts, to be honest with you. There are so many people in Europe who are shorter than I am, who can start a lot quicker than I can, but, even for the short distance of 60 metres, I'm a lot better than they are.

Your physique is an advantage?
Good things come in big packages! The bigger the diamond the more it's worth. Obviously, the shorter you are, the shorter your legs usually are and the quicker you can turn them round, but you've got to have the strength and the power to get from A to B which is what matters. I'm more powerful than they are. To lose a few inches, a few yards over the first ten metres doesn't really matter as long as I can gain a few yards over the last 40 or 50 metres. It doesn't make any difference at all.

Have you worked very hard on the start and breaking down races into sections?
You've got to work hard at anything. There's always

aspects of our race that you can work on and you work on your weaknesses as well as trying to develop your strengths. We break things down. We look at things on videos and everything and we say: this is where I lost it, this is where we think I can improve. With most people, once they've perfected everything they stop. You always find different aspects of a racing programme which you can improve on. Ron and I still believe that I can get better over the start, that I can gain more over the first 30, 40 metres, than I am at the moment.

Are you aiming for the perfect start?
No, there's no such thing as a perfect start. You just work on trying to react as quick as possible to the gun, and to get your legs turning over as fast as possible. You know it's not perfect and it can never be perfect. You can't move faster than the gun, so the gun's always there to beat you. You can get it as close to perfection as possible, but never perfect.

■ Perfection, the unachievable goal. For a young athlete, seeing an Olympic champion still striving for it, is an inspiration. But this pursuit of perfection is potentially damaging. Ian Wilson is an extremely talented athlete. Some say he is talented enough to be rated the world's third fastest free style 1500 metres swimmer in February, 1993.

Wilson had the potential to become, like Christie, the best in the world. And he had the commitment. His speciality requires both speed and stamina. And without dedication, competitors are better off out of the water. Lack of dedication was not a problem for Ian Wilson, either.

But over-training was. In February, 1993, having improved steadily throughout his career, Wilson began to feel tired after sessions. At this early stage in his career, this was unusual, particularly as he usually had stamina in abundance. Of course, Wilson knew his event was tough and that he would suffer pain in the course of a 1500 metres swim. But after 300 metres?

By June he was sick. His heart rate was, for an athlete competing at his level, sky high and his hormones were fluctuating wildly. His doctor ordered him to reduce dramatically his training programme. Wilson had massively over-trained and, while the doctors advised him to continue doing a small amount of excercise as part of his recuperation, he had to scratch from all competition, including the European Championships. He was, to coin a well-worn sporting cliché, gutted.

He has since recovered, but it was a slow and torturous process. He had to build up gradually from a modest base and, instead of working flat out, mixed weeks of light training with heavier work. It seems to have saved one very talented individual from the sporting scrap heap.

The subject of over-training is not one that Ian Wilson is comfortable with. For a career athlete, the experience was difficult to comprehend, particularly as Wilson's

*Linford Christie —
'Everybody remembers the guy who wins. Whoever said "It's not the winning, it's the taking part that counts," was a loser.'*

response to failure had always been to work harder at his sport. Ian's mother noticed it first. She recalls that he was constantly tired, and occasionally bad tempered. Mrs Wilson helps her son by clocking his work-outs and she became reluctant to tell him the times he was recording for fear of his reaction. At the time, she thought that it was her fault, that they were simply too bad to be true. When she did tell him, his instincts told him to get back in the water, to work harder, to strive for greater fitness. It was a disastrous strategy. ▶

Learning the hard way. Ian Wilson came close to collapse with chronic fatigue before he learnt the secrets of a scientific training régime.

Q. How did the over-training manifest itself in competition?
IAN WILSON: I suffered pains in my arms, heavy breathing, real fatigue, all only at

the very beginning of a 1500 metre race. If you look at the event lasting some 15 minutes, if you dive in and swim for about three minutes, you don't expect to be in agony then, which I was. So, obviously, I knew there was something drastically up. I had some initial blood tests taken by the Swimming Association's doctor and then I was referred to the British Olympic Medical Centre where I saw Dr Richard Budgett and he diagnosed me as suffering from chronic fatigue syndrome, from training at too high an intensity with insufficient recovery built into the programme. It had caused some muscle damage.

How did you feel?
It's difficult to describe, but, at the time, I didn't really feel in control of my stroke. I felt as though my stroke had gone. The aches and the pains and the heaviness in my arms, laboured breathing, high pulse rate, high resting pulse rate, my body was just, altogether not right. The event, the 1500 metres, racing hard for 15 minutes, is the longest Olympic swimming event, and getting in there and racing hard and pushing your body for 15 minutes doesn't do it that much good when you are in such a state. I saw the doctor in London and was told that I had to withdraw from the European team. It was quite ironic that the day that I saw the doctor there was the press release day for the Great Britain Swim Team for the 1993 championship. Obviously, I was shell-shocked to say the least - everything that I'd been working towards that year had just been taken away. It was very hard and very difficult to take at first, but then, from that point, I put everything into the hands of the doctor and whatever he recommended for me to follow over the next few months I agreed to. Whatever advice he was willing to give, I was willing to go along with because he did stress that I was in a really bad state when I went down to see him.

What might have happened if you had carried on training?
The doctor said that if I hadn't received medical advice, then my condition would have got a lot worse. I could have ended up with something possibly like ME where you can hardly stand up and walk across the room. That was quite a sobering thought, so really it was a case of following his advice. He said that scientific evidence had proved that the best way to help your body to readjust was to do very, very light gentle exercise, so I went from swimming two two-hour sessions every day to following the doctor's plan and doing 20 minutes every other day. It was a case of just getting in the water, plodding up and down just like the general public do, keeping my heart rate controlled and monitored, and feeling nice and steady and really just getting into some light exercise. It was a case of slowly building up from that, so we were looking, in conjunction with the doctor, to work on the amount of time that was spent in the water, then the number of times per week in the water, and eventually work on the intensity.

Was cutting back on training easy?
I thought it would feel worse than it did. Obviously, you dedicate your day to training,

getting up at 5 o'clock in the morning to swim for two hours between 5.30am and 7.30am, before going off to university. I'd come back and swim for another two hours in the evening, and then, fit in circuit training, weight training, and land conditioning. I went from doing that to doing 20 minutes every other day. I thought I'd be pulling my hair out and, at the beginning, I think I was a little bit frustrated, but it was giving me something to look forward to; having that 20 minutes planned every other day ensured that I had something to look forward to and base my day around.

Now in tune with his body, Ian Wilson has re-entered the arena of international competition.

Was yours a bad case?
The doctors said it's quite a relative sort of thing, but if you're pushing your body to such an extent, there's really only a fine line that you can push it to, and I'm the sort of person who likes to give 110 per cent in whatever I do. I think, really, it was a case of getting the sessions from coaching and trying to work as hard as I could. It's difficult really because, for the event I do, there's no excuse. You've got to get in there and you've got to train hard. You've got to do the yardage at the end of the week and you've got to do the intensity. You don't expect, at the end of a swimming week, having done 11 two-hour swimming sessions, three weight training exercises, and swim bench exercises, to be feeling great and relaxed. You're bound to be feeling a little bit tired. I think, really, that I was just getting into a routine of being constantly tired so I wasn't really aware of how bad I was getting. I think people around me were noticing; my mood swings, I got grumpy quite, quite easily, moody, really really tired, tired to look at. But it's just a case of pushing yourself hard to get there. You don't make an Olympic final from just turning up a couple of sessions a week and doing nothing - you've got to get in there and you've got to work hard at it.

How has your programme changed?
You do need the high sort of yardage I was doing behind you, but the key is the intensity that you're putting in. Now, it's a case of trying to listen to my body a bit more. I monitor my heart-rate, last thing at night and first thing in the morning. I take my resting pulse rate, log it down to see if there's any sort of deviation. If I wake up at 5 o'clock on the morning and it's sky high, obviously that's alarm bells sounding. My body, at that moment in time, may be coming down with a cold or a virus or something. At one time, I would have planned to go in and get a good session done. Maybe now I think I am better off having that session off. Also, I think as you get older you don't need the same intense sort of workload because you are looking at each year, having had the previous year's block of hard work behind you. The bottom line is listening to your body a lot more. I am the sort of a person who if I wanted to get 10 or 11 swimming sessions in a week, I would get them come hell or high water, but now I think it's important to listen to your body and if your body is crying out that there's something up, then there's no harm, there's no shame, there's no disgrace in having a session off to try and let your body come up to a better level.

■ The moral of this story - apart from the obvious one that mum always knows best - is that training is not simply a case of hours in the pool, on the road, in the gym, on the track. In fact, over-training can be as potentially damaging to an athlete's winning prospects as under-training. For Ian Wilson as well as the likes of Linford Christie.

In distance events, where stamina is tested as extensively as speed, this presents competitors with a testing mental challenge; knowing when enough is enough. Most are dedicated sportsmen and women who sacrifice a great deal in the chase for gold or records. The conscience plays on such individuals who, perhaps, fear more than anything that "they have done less training" than an arch rival and are relatively under-prepared.

The mind alone is unlikely to be strong enough to persuade the committed (and sometimes blinkered) athlete to walk away from the track for a break. They must look at their results and listen to their bodies. In a sport where the individual is the whole, the constituent parts, the calves, the arms, the chest, the lungs, and the heart have the ability to warn the brain. And the athlete must heed the signals.

For distance athletes like Yvonne Murray, the importance of this is difficult to overstate. Ignore the signs of over-training and Murray could end up seriously injured, particularly as she plans to move up in distance to challenge the 10000 metres elite at the 1996 Olympics. The new discipline requires her to run more than three times the distance she has been competing at for the majority of her career and the simple logic that recommends a trebling of her training is seriously misguided.

But the acceptance of the need to respect the limits of the body presents the stamina specialist with something of a dilemma; how to ensure that the competitor is sufficiently prepared without putting at risk short term performance and long term health. Only by adopting a regime that will keep her fit AND healthy can Yvonne Murray fulfil her - or more specifically - her body's potential. Every second at the track, in the gym or wherever her preparation takes place, must therefore be made to count. Training must be efficient.

One of Murray's solutions to the distance runner's dilemma provokes a few sniggers at the swimming pool, but at least it saves her joints. Murray wears an aqua suit for jogging in the water. In 1989, prior to discovering the life of a water baby, Murray was happiest on a bicycle that went nowhere. The exercise bike was her salvation. It also helped that she was able to use it in a greenhouse to create the environment similar to the oppressive heat of Tokyo, where the 1991 World Championships were being held. She made the switch to aqua jogging as underwater running was even more efficient than pedalling.

Tommy Boyle, her coach, has been responsible for most of the innovations in Murray's personalised training regime. He has made sure that every hour Murray spends training is a well spent hour. There is no waste and everything is geared towards her event and its demands. In the past, this has included weight training, circuits in the gym, treadmill work, some altitude training (although the results suggested it did not

work for her), and a month off!

This last treat highlights the importance modern athletes attach to the quality of training. There is little point in pounding the streets in search of extra stamina if, by doing so, Murray contracts a virus. She may as well go away on holiday. Murray, and her colleagues in the modern athletics world listen to their bodies to avoid the suffering of over-training that Ian Wilson was the unfortunate victim of. ▶

Long distance runners place their bodies under immense unnatural strains in the quest for success. If Yvonne Murray ignores the signs of over-training she could ruin her chances of a healthy life after her athletic career.

Q. What determines your training programme for the day, or if, indeed, you train at all?
YVONNE MURRAY: The routine I've established since 1987 is to get up and take my pulse before I'm fully awake, if it's possible, and then weigh myself. The good thing about taking my pulse is - I've passed this tip on to many athletes who now use heart monitors - that you're able to check it every morning and if it jumps five or six beats then you're obviously fatigued from the session you did the night before or possibly going down with some flu virus or whatever. You can change your session accordingly so you don't push yourself further under.

Is this before you switch the alarm clock off?
You try and monitor your heart before the alarm goes off because, otherwise, you tend to find it's not a natural sleep that you get. I seem to have this internal body clock. I tell my mind the night before what time I want to get up in the morning, so I very rarely use

an alarm clock, because it's not a natural waking up process and your heart tends to jump.

When did you start doing this?
In the days before I joined Tommy Boyle in 1987, I never did anything like it. I used to train hard, every single day, and my body used to break down.

Has science has played a large role in your training?
I think it's vital for me. When I joined Tommy, it was a complete shock to my system. I had never had a physiologist, and I had never run on a treadmill in my life before. Now, I actually find it gives me a lot of confidence because I know that my training schedules are specific to my event. There's no waste. I think science is playing a very important role more and more in athletics. Distances are getting longer and times are getting faster so athletes are, therefore, training much harder. They need to use science to minimise the number of foot strikes, especially in my event and moving up to 10,000 metres. If you can do a session on a treadmill or in the pool that's going to alleviate a lot of stress and then obviously that's an advantage.

Yvonne Murray's training has undergone a scientific revolution. Every aspect of her life is under the close scrutiny of her physiology back-up team.

Do you devote the majority of your time to quality training?
I want to feel as fit when I leave the sport as when I entered it. The training is geared to getting the maximum benefit from the minimum amount of training. For example, in the past, most people, when they saw me running in the pool, associated it with training for someone who has got an injury. People are using it as an actual session, because you get the same effect from running in the pool as you do when you're running outside but you have less foot strikes on hard ground and there's less chance of you getting injured.

Does this mean you do less miles than other athletes?
Yes, it's quite interesting when I go to major championships and everyone's sitting round a table and discussing how many miles they've done in that particular week. It horrifies me to think that some girls do 120 miles a week. I'm doing maybe about 50 at the most, so therefore for me to improve, I just do more. If you're doing 120 miles a week already, what on earth are you going to have to do to improve?

Does doing less miles make you feel guilty?
I used to panic. But, it came home to me more and more, what are these girls who are

doing very high mileage going to do to improve? Do they have to put more miles on? I believe more in quality than quantity. And I want to be running in another five, six, seven years time. Everyone is different. I prefer to do four miles hard than ten miles at a steady pace.

Aqua jogging is a good example of your preference for quality over quantity?
A lot of footballers who are injured wear wet vests to keep them afloat in the pool. An aqua jogger which keeps you afloat in the water just enables you to run as well. It's caused quite a stir actually when people saw me in the water in the deep end for the first time. A few kids came up to me and said: "If you can't swim you shouldn't be in the deep end".

And the treadmill helps, too?
I think beforehand I was a little bit apprehensive of using it. Most people in the winter use indoor running competitions to gauge how well they're performing. I decided not to do that and use the treadmill instead. It was new, so, obviously I was a bit apprehensive about it.

■ Yvonne Murray is engaged to a fellow athlete who runs for her club in Scotland. Undoubtedly, she hopes to enjoy a full family life after a career of achievement in athletics. She has already gone some way to achieving the last ambition with a bronze medal in the Olympics and gold in the Indoor World Championships when they were held in Toronto.

She does, however, want to finish with athletics and still be able to enjoy the remaining forty odd years of her life. After all, she has reasonable expectations of spending more time off the track than she will on it, particularly if age and infirmities take a hold long before the stamina she displays during a race suggests they should.

The combination of training and Murray's naturally super-efficient cardiovascular system makes regular heart scans an important safety factor. Over expansion of the heart could lead to it becoming dangerously constricted within the chest cavity.

Heart scans are usually associated with the unfit, but Murray has hers "imaged" regularly. It is an extreme example of listening to your body - more a question of getting it to talk - with the aim of ensuring that the athlete is equipped to deal with the demands of training for the Olympics, the World Championships or any other event where the search on the training ground is for the body's absolute limits. It also reveals if Murray is putting herself in danger by exercising too single-mindedly. It protects her long-term interests.

For Murray, the heart scanner, a bit like going to the cinema with your heart's image as the star show, is no less important than the treadmill. It all helps to ensure that her training is of value and not misguided, as well as monitoring her general well-being with life away from the track in mind. It ensures that Yvonne Murray - with some help from Tommy Boyle - gets the maximum out of herself, without forgetting her future away

Graeme Obree takes a scientific stance toward training, but rejects the use of hi-tech monitoring equipment. 'No instrument is accurate enough to tell me exactly how my body feels.'

from the world of international athletics. ▶

Q. When did you first get your heart imaged?

YVONNE MURRAY: When I joined Tommy, he wanted to check that everything was fine. You hear a lot of frightening stories on the news about sports people who have collapsed, possibly with heart problems, who never knew they had a problem. You don't expect someone who is extremely fit to have heart problems. I went through a series of examinations and fitness testing before I even embarked on the training schedule Tommy first set me. It's just like anyone in the street who wants to start up sport, they go to their doctor for a physical. I had to do the same.

What was it like?

It was quite a eye opener for me because I hadn't had it done before. To see your heart on the screen was a bit scary, but it gave me peace of mind to know that everything was fine. We've repeated it periodically as I've progressed with training and the training's got harder. The bottom line was I wanted to finish in athletics as fit as when I started - or as healthy as when I started.

Do a lot of athletes neglect long-term considerations?

I would imagine so. You push your body to such an extreme. Athletes are highly competitive. Sometimes you run through injuries and do damage to your body that you don't really think about at the time. I've been very fortunate because of my scientific back-up. Everything is monitored so that I'm not really overstepping the mark and pushing my body to extremes. You hear of top athletes getting ME and various illnesses due to excessive training. For me, having the scientific back-up means I've been very fortunate. And a lot of people have commented on that. If something does happen I've got someone to go to immediately. Athletes like myself are sometimes the world's worst for saying "I've got a niggle, but I'll just forget about it, it'll go away in a couple of days". And then it progresses and progresses till it reaches the stage where you need to have six months off. It's sometimes quite hard. Tommy sometimes steps in and says, look, you just can't run. It's very hard, but having someone there to tell you to stop is helpful.

Do you find not running harder than running?

It is an addiction. I enjoy it, but when I'm injured I don't because I become a bear and that's because I have a build up of energy and can't get rid of it.

In line with sports scientists, Obree realises that fitness comes not from training, but through recovering from training.

■ Graeme Obree is less reliant on technology than Yvonne Murray, but has essentially followed her in refining his training so that he maximises the benefits. He shares with her a need to develop stamina for his event, pursuit cycling, a gruelling discipline that defies the romantic notions most people associate with his own special mode of athletic transport. He also aims to enjoy a happy life after racing, with someone who won't expect him to cycle miles and miles every week.

Obree is a world class cyclist, who is perhaps best known for developing a revolutionary new racing position. This is unfair. It pays insufficient respect to Obree's achievements which includes a world pursuit championship title and a 4000 metres world record. After all, there must be more to him than where he sits in the saddle.

Obree's training programme is an effort to maximise the return from hours spent preparing for competition on the bike. And on the bike is the only place he trains. He attempts to recreate racing conditions for training based on the logic that you must devote yourself to specific preparation if you want to be the world's number one cyclist. As little time as possible is wasted on developing muscles that might not be of use to him in a cycle race.

Obree approached cycling technique equally methodically. He broke the discipline down into its constituent parts to devise his own unique approach that has proved so effective. He arrived at the conclusion that only wind resistance and the power output of the rider were factors in determining how fast a cyclist could go in equal competition. This prompted a search for a more aerodynamic position that lead him to lowering his seat position and adopting a hunched riding posture with his elbows under the body. Obree believes that it means he is using all of his leg muscles to propel the bike forward. Although no tests have been carried out to prove this, the clock hints that there is some substance in the argument.

Obree's self-confidence led him to question the basic principles of cycling technique. It is a quality that has impressed national coach, Doug Dailey, and countless journalists well used to dealing with athletes who believe in their own qualities, sometimes to a degree that is not matched by subsequent career achievements.

Obree's single-mindedness extends to training. His schedule is based on a belief that time spent off the bike is wasted time for cyclists. All training, even weight training, is done on the bike. It is an extreme version of what most cyclist coaches believe and recommend - high intensity, short duration, practise of skills only used in competition and only when fully recovered from previous sessions. He departs from normal coaching convention in the degree to which he specialises and his rejection of interval training - "it just makes you good at intervals" - a corner stone of most cyclists' preparation for major championships. This type of training - completing a set distance, resting for a set time, and then repeating this a set number of times hardly features in his programme.

Like Murray, Obree listens to his body, but in a much less sophisticated way. Crudely speaking, if he does not feel like training he will not do any. Without his self-belief, it is

For Obree, training time off the bike is wasted time. His central philosophy is that he must train his body to do exactly what it needs to do in competition.

doubtful that such a regime would work. Athletes are, by and large, too paranoid. But, once again, the clock indicates that it does. His only concession to self-doubt is that he cannot rely on his own judgement from an armchair. He always has to force himself into the saddle to decide. This is a comforting sign that Obree is sometimes afflicted by that very human element present in all athletes, laziness. ▶

Q. What does your training involve?
GRAEME OBREE: It's based on a sort of logic that I realised a few years ago; that your body recovers more specifically to training than most coaches or the scientific community realise. If you train for one minute hard your body'll recover in a way that makes you good at going for one minute hard. It was previously thought that if you go for one minute hard that's good for going any distance on a bicycle. But, I realised it wasn't quite like that. If you ride for 100 miles at a steady state, steady pace, and you do that every day, you make yourself good at doing 100 miles every day. But if you are competing in short races, there's no way 100 miles a day is going to do you any good whatsoever, because you don't have that pressure of the short burst. It's very specific. The more specific your training is, the better. Basically, my training is simulating the pursuit effort, which is a four and a half minute effort, as hard as I can humanly go.

So your training is very event specific?
Most athletes these days do some sort of strength training which involves weights and things, but I don't go with the theory that you do weights and get stronger. You do, but not specifically. I do specific weight training, which involves basically on-your-bike weight training. Weight training only makes you good at weight training. If you're trying to develop a specific muscle in your leg then you don't know if that muscle's getting more training than another muscle that's also used. There's a weak link in every chain. If you do specific weights, or tried to do specific weight training off the bike for each muscle, you wouldn't know one muscle was stronger than the other. With my training, you know that every muscle's getting the exact strain that it would do under racing conditions.

Do you monitor your fitness using anything other than the clock?
No instrument is accurate enough to tell me exactly how my body feels. Because there's other things that influence your heart rate, heat build up, a virus, or anything, I wouldn't rely on the clock purely as a means of saying how fast I should go on my training.

How do you know when to stop training?
My training is totally different from tradition because the traditional attitude is that the more training you manage to squeeze in a week, the better. For me, that is totally illogical, because, basically you don't get fitter by training, you get fitter by recovering from training. If I can train for a short period and then recover fully from that training

then my body will end up stronger than it would have had it been weakened by over-training.

What is your routine?
I don't decide if I'm going to train until I've left the house on my bike because you can't decide until you're on the bike and pedalling. You'll know then if your body's still recovering or if it's fully recovered and then you can train again. It's harder not to train than to train. Training for an athlete is the most natural and easiest thing to do. I know some people have tried my method and they end up with anxiety because they don't feel they've trained enough. They always have to feel that tiredness in their body. I know that if I overdo it, which I've done in the past, what the consequences will be in the long run.

■ If Steve Backley could throw javelins every day, he would be unique to his event. Javelin throwing exerts such a force on the body that an athlete is ill-advised to throw any more frequently than is required to keep technique finely honed.

Backley has not been unduly affected by these limitations which, although the same for every javelin thrower, apply to him more so, as a consequence of a broken elbow, when he was 14, and recurring shoulder trouble. He has held the world record

Obree questions even the rudiments of his sport. His radical position on the bike has caused controversy, but he maintains that it is both physically and aerodynamically more efficient than any other.

four times, won the European Championship, the Commonwealth Games and an Olympic bronze in Barcelona. So much for the adage, "practise makes perfect".

Injuries are a way of life for Backley. They have affected his social life - "constant pain and anti-inflammatory drugs all summer, once" - and his day-to-day routine to the extent that over the last few years he has sometimes struggled to remember what it was like to be fit and well. ▶

Q. What are the main stresses for a javelin thrower?
STEVE BACKLEY: Where *doesn't* it stress? I think it's from my right ear lobe to my left toenail. It seems to be up the left hand side of your body to your hips and then sort of swop sides to the right side of your body and your upper body. Elbows, shoulders, knees, lower back, you name it really. If you asked someone to devise an event that would wreck your body he would probably come up with something similar to javelin throwing. Avoiding injury is half way to winning major championships. About nine out of ten competitors on the day have got a problem and it usually interferes with technique and distance.

Is there a particular injury that is common to javelin throwers?
The shoulder seems to take a pretty bad bashing. Fatima Whitbread, the former top British female thrower, had to give the event up because of a very major shoulder problem. At some point, every javelin thrower's going to get a problem with their arm, whether it be shoulder, or elbow, just because of the nature of the event.

Coach John Trower works with Steve Backley to achieve 'Unconscious Competence' — the ability of the body to perform the technically perfect throw automatically.

What are the injuries that you've had to cope with?
I ruptured the rotator cuff, which is the socket part of the shoulder. I basically nicked it throwing and caused some inflammation because it's such an intricate, tightly compact area. If you get an injury somewhere and then compensate for it, it'll shift somewhere else and then you'll compensate again and you can go round in one big vicious circle if you're not careful. I've learnt that, if I get hurt, I'll stop. I spent the best part of two years not really getting to the bottom of it.

How did this affect you mentally?

You start thinking, have I prepared properly? Because you've missed some training you think, have I had the technical background to be able to compete here? You've got to be super-confident of your own abilities. It comes down to you knowing your technique.

How do you keep going mentally?

When everything's going well, it's easy. When everything's looking good and you're training day-to-day and making progress, you get a positive sort of self-image and feel nice. Then you get an injury and things just start to look less comfortable. There's a

negative self-image you start to create. You can actually consciously feel yourself thinking negative thoughts and they're so destructive to your training, preparation, and competing.

Is there any training you can do when you are injured?

You are very unlucky if you have injuries at both ends of your body and javelin throwers can either work on their upper bodies, or do a lot of running. If you get a problem in your elbow or shoulder, you just do more running. There are occasions where you know it hurts at both ends and then you do very little, but you can always stretch and keep supple and just bide your time. There are a lot of people who want instant success and it can be very frustrating if you're in good shape and pick up a small niggle, but it is very important just to take it easy and concentrate on the other things; some stretching to avoid injury. The key is in *avoiding* injury.

'If you asked someone to devise an event that would wreck your body, he would probably come up with something similar to javelin throwing.'

How does injury affect your technique?

Javelin throwing is a lot about balance and technique, shifting your body weight and controlling your centre of gravity. If you are injured it can throw you slightly off balance and then you're just not going to get the result.

■ Backley takes the art of minimalising training waste to another level. The demands that the act of throwing make on a body already ravaged by injury means that there is a limit to the number of actual throws he can do on the training ground; so he practices in his head. This technique, known as "visualisation", involves the athlete performing the perfect throw in his or her mind. Backley used to use the technique only when he was unable to throw through injury but has subsequently incorporated it into his training schedule on a daily basis.

It also helps him prepare for throwing in major competition. Javelin championships can demand that athletes wait for up to 45 minutes before they are called to perform. During this time, even the most confident technician can be afflicted by nerves and self doubt. The only way through this unforgiving three quarters of an hour, maintains Backley, is by "visualisation", by going through the routine of competition in your mind. ▶

How do you manage to keep your training going when you were too injured to train physically?

Visualising a throw plays a big part. When you get injured, it's quite a nice way of rehearsing the technique, even though, obviously, you can't get out there and throw if you're hurt. You can do maybe 1000 throws in the armchair at home, and you know you're never going to get hurt. You're not going to overstrain any part of yourself, any of your muscles or the soft tissue in your body. You're just training the neuro pathways. It's been proved that you're learning the technique of javelin throwing or whatever event, just by simulating it in your brain, thinking it through, thinking the rhythms. You can even simulate a situation like the last round of a championship final, and put the pressure on yourself. If you monitor it, your heart rate will go up. When you get to the major championship and you're put in that stressful situation it's no surprise, so you're totally in control. You've done it a thousand times in your head. It's just doing it again.

How easy is it to achieve good visualisation?

Ideally you want to be either lying on your bed, or just hanging out somewhere comfortable in a sort of symmetrical position. You could even be walking down the street, or driving along in the car. The main thing is that you just switch in and visualise the techniques of your event. You try to visualise the ultimate throw, which for me would involve certain physical positions, timings, rhythms, balance. You'd see them all come together in your mind in a throw and then the javelin would go out the other end of the stadium.

To visualise a perfect throw in his mind, Backley must have a detailed memory of every aspect of an ideal performance.

When you're injured, do you find that the visualisation is as easy as when you are fit, or does it take more concentration?

When you're injured, it's more difficult because, although you're dreaming, a lot of it is memory. If you've done a throwing session, say, at a weekend, then on the Tuesday or Wednesday of that week it will be very easy to visualise because you just remember the positions from the weekend, correcting little bits and pieces. When you're hurt and have not thrown for a while, the first time you visualise a throw it's fairly strong in your mind, then your memory becomes gradually more and more diluted until you throw again.

Is it important in real competitive situations?

Once, in actual competition, I just couldn't see what I was doing, I couldn't see the event, and I was very disappointed because I hadn't done the proper mental preparation. I was quite negative. I learnt the hard way. It was in Tokyo in 1991, and I failed to qualify when really it shouldn't have been a problem. I tried to throw just over the qualification length. I didn't think about relaxing and seeing the correct rhythms, I thought about the outcome goal. The psychologist would have waved a finger and said "no, no, no, no outcome goals, it's all process goals and performance goals." You *know* the technique positions; you've got to tune into those. If you see yourself standing on the rostrum before the event, then you're history. It happens. The guys do well in qualification and then come back the next day for the finals and you know they've already written their winning speech and they just go to pieces. They lose the sort of visualisation of the process towards the outcome. It's quite important in a competition to visualise the perfect throw. It's the pressure situation and, when the pressure's on, it's almost harder to see what you're doing because your adrenalin's flowing and you tend to rush things. It's very important to slow them down and see in your mind's eye, when you're visualising things in real time. I think what a lot of athletes get carried away with, especially in a competitive situation, is the

outcome goal - what winning will bring you - it's never the way to do it.

■ Backley aims to achieve what he describes as "unconscious competence", or perfection in his own mind. This is hardly a technique based on science. It does not require sophisticated equipment that has only recently become available to athletes. Backley merely requires an armchair and some peace and quiet.

What it does reflect is a modern approach to training that aims to get the most out of an athlete within the parameters set by the physical limitations of the body.

Athletics training is no longer simply a case of putting in the hours, the miles, the sessions. The amount of training is less of a consideration for athletes at world level where a high yield from time with one's coach is vital to winning medals. What matters is quality training.

The extreme case of Ian Wilson highlights the dangers of training based purely on volume. It is a case of an individual's admirably determined search for excellence ultimately destroying performance. For athletes involved in endurance events like long distance swimming it is particularly difficult to reconcile the very human need to feel as though they are training hard with the scientific evidence that suggests shorter training sessions, more events-specific in content, are of greater benefit. An athlete needs the indestructible self-belief of Graeme Obree that, for him, on any one day, he is better served by not training than by training.

800 metre Contender Martin Steele believes that his bio-rhythms dictate the quality of his performance. Scientists may disagree, but ultimately his conviction, right or wrong, could make the difference between a gold or silver medal.

With Steve Backley, and to a lesser extent Yvonne Murray, this conviction comes from the realisation that the demands of their discipline require them to maximise the return from training. It is no good Backley striving to achieving the perfect throw time after time in deserted stadiums, prior to competition; he would leave his best shot on the training ground and probably get injured in the process. He must do it in his head. Murray would destroy her ability to perform by pounding the track, she must get into her aqua jogger and join the sniggering school children in the swimming pool!

Obree, Murray and Backley listen to their bodies; Murray to the beat of her early morning pulse, Backley to the twinge in his shoulder, elbow, groin, or wherever the next injury is threatening to strike, and Obree to gut feelings. All three do so to get the greatest return from time spent training. Backley practising throwing the javelin in his armchair is the most extreme example of the growing trend in athletics where improving the quality of training around the event through technology, or self awareness, is the key

THE MAIN CONTENDERS

LINFORD CHRISTIE
Date of Birth: 2 April 1960
Height: 6' 2½" / 1.89 m
Weight: 14st 7lbs / 92 kg

COMPETITION RECORD:
100m: 1993 World champion;
       1993, 1991, 1989, 1987 European
       Cup champion;
       1992 Olympic champion;
       1992, 1989 World Cup champion;
       1990, 1986 European champion;
       1990 Commonwealth champion;
       1988 Olympic silver;
       1987 World bronze;
       1986 Commonwealth silver.

60m: 1991 World Indoor silver;
       1990, 1988 European Indoor champion.

200m: 1991 World Indoor silver;
       1986 European Indoor champion.

to success. It makes "no pain, no gain" sound as dated as a Christmas Number One.

In a sport where competitors are encouraged to reach for the stars, it may be appropriate to mention Martin Steele as well as Obree, Murray and Backley. He shares their conviction that training must be efficient, but he is guided by lunar cycles and biorhythm charts. Steele is an 800 metre runner. Up until 1993 he had been a talented athlete without ever threatening to hit the big time. He met Richard Hepworth in 1992 and by the middle of the next year had recorded the best time in the world for his event. Like Obree, Murray and Backley, he only trains when he is feeling good. Steele, however, bases his plans around the peaks and troughs of three cycles - concentration, co-ordination/confidence and strength - with peak activity programmed to take place at favourable times in each for the individual athlete.

The three biorhythm lines which Steele bases his training on are derived from the more well known "intellectual, emotional and physical cycles". Steele gauges his well-being by checking his personal charts, prepared by Hepworth. The charts indicate when he is strongest and best equipped for the most punishing of training sessions, when he is at his sharpest, and ready to run competitively, and when he is below par, and should be resting.

Hepworth also believes that an athlete's date of birth is crucial to his chances of top-level success: "Anyone born in October is bound to run well in the summer". (Yvonne Murray was, incidentally, born in that month.) The importance of this belief is that major athletics championships are usually in mid summer, when October babies are most likely to achieve a triple peak in their cycles, an optimum time to compete.

Hepworth is partly supported in his belief by others. In a letter published in *Nature*, Dr Ad Dudink, a psychologist at Amsterdam University, claimed that the month a baby is born in could dictate whether he or she becomes a great sportsman or woman. Although the correspondence did appear in the April edition of the respected scientific journal, it was not published on the first of the month. The statistics are quite compelling. The best Dutch tennis players are mostly born in the first three months of the year while top footballers are often born in August with the previous month, July, something of a complete write-off. In Britain, according to Dr Dudink, the best footballers are born in September and October with five of England manager Terry Venables' first new-look team which played against Denmark having birthdays in those months.

If Hepworth had blown his own trumpet and attempted to make a financial killing with his theories on the back of his disciple's success, fellow athletes might be well advised to steer clear of them. This however is not the case. Indeed, Hepworth is happy to share his work with athletes of all codes in the hope that standards in sport will improve accordingly.

Steele is adamant that they work. He relates: "You've got to be sceptical about something so revolutionary, but I used to crawl off the track three times a week and fall out of bed the next morning. That has all changed. I feel great."

To sceptics Steele may be no more than confirmation that athletics is a sport rich with eccentrics who will clutch at anything they believe will enhance their ability to win. But his performances have improved dramatically and he has a right to claim that the proof of the pudding is in the eating. Whatever the scientific rights and wrongs of his method, he is certainly an interesting example of the growing trend in athletics that has seen the "sergeant major" school of drill training replaced by the more philosophical "less can mean more" approach.

Great news, too, for Scorpios and Libras.

FILMING LINFORD CHRISTIE

Linford Christie is a phenomenal force on the track: at 6' 2½" and 14 stone he dwarfs most other sprinters and seems to crunch over the athletics field like a giant, tearing through 100 metres with the brutal energy of a tornado. One of the focuses of his training and the key to his success is his start. Not naturally built for speed out of the blocks, he has devoted hours, weeks and months to achieving the explosive power at the gun he now commands. When we decided to film him, it was this incredible starting eruption, where every muscle in his body explodes with energy, that we wanted to capture.

The difficulty is that it's over so quickly. Linford likes to say he goes on the B of the bang, and certainly the initial impulses of his start are over in hundredths of a second. This gave us a technical problem. We had decided to film all the hi-speed photography for the series on super 16mm film. This gives an image slightly wider than a TV screen which has to be "letterboxed" for transmission - edged on top and bottom with black - but it's a format much closer in shape to the images seen by the eye and hence much more pleasing to look at. However, it is new technology and we were working at its limits. The fastest the film can be made to run in a camera is 150 frames per second - played back at the standard 25 fps of TV broadcasting, this means that action is slowed down six times. But six times was not slow enough to capture the instant explosive energy of Christie's starts. Instead we moved back to standard 16mm film - a tried and trusted technology for which speeds of over 10,000 frames per second are possible. We settled on filming the bigger close-ups of Christie's body reacting to the starter's gun at 300 frames each second - replayed, this would make his ferocious start last 12 times its natural length - revealing for the first time the almost mechanical workings of the engineering masterpiece that is an athlete's body.

What with all this technical deliberation, we forgot one very pertinent fact. At the Linford Christie stadium, where we were due to film on windy exposed ground in West London, in spring, it is cold. In fact, it's *very* cold. For world class athletes, cold is a deadly enemy - it knots muscles and shortens tendons - pulling and damaging any unprepared muscle. There was no way we would be able to film the high-speed images of Christie's exposed muscles there. He could never risk the damage he might do, the best we could have hoped for would be detailed close-ups of his fleece training trousers!

When we realised our problem we desperately searched our diaries for alternative filming days and locations. The life of an international athlete like Christie is organised months in advance and filled with immovable engagements, endorsements, advert film shoots, photocalls, and of course, training. Fortunately for us, there was a window - at Linford's training camp in Florida in late April - hopefully warm enough to allow training in one of the skin suits that he has made famous.

When the day arrived it was, indeed, bright and warm. All the waiting, we think, was worthwhile.

R.D.

FILMING GRAHAM OBREE

We filmed Graham Obree twice for the series. Once in Bordeaux at the end of 1993 and again at Herne Hill in South London in the spring of 1994. At the time we first met, Graham had turned the world of cycling on its head. He had risen from obscurity to smash cycling's most coveted record (for distance covered in one hour) in less than six months. The record, set by Francisco Moser, the grand old man of cycling, had stood for over 9 years and Obree's breaking of it by more than 400 metres was akin to Mike Powell's smashing of Bob Beamon's 20 year old long-jump record, or the breaking by Roger Bannister of the four minute mile. Even more importantly Obree had won the world pursuit championship, de-throning the acknowledged king of pursuit cycling - Olympic Gold Medallist Chris Boardman, who himself had sent shock waves through the

Filming Graeme Obree was fraught with problems...

Filming Graham Obree

cycling world with his use of a new design of carbon fibre cycle at the Barcelona Olympics. Despite all this, Obree was delightfully untainted by his success. We interviewed him in a cluttered hotel room in Bordeaux where he was waiting for a three stage head-to-head pursuit race with his arch rival Chris Boardman. Obree lay casually amongst newspaper cuttings, bits of cycle and the rainbow coloured vests of a cycling world champion, and shared with us his thoughts on training, on bike design and on the future of the sport. He was enchanting to listen to. We hoped very much that this

charming and brilliant young Scotsman wouldn't be jaded and subdued by a career in what is a terrifyingly exacting professional sport.

When we met him again in the spring of 1994 at Herne Hill cycle track in South London our fears were unfounded. This time we wanted to film Graham on the unique cycle he had built himself using parts from an old washing machine and on which he had ridden into sporting history. The only problem was the weather: whenever we were ready to film, hailstorms would appear from nowhere, forcing us off the track and into the shelter of the old draughty stadium. It also wreaked havoc on the four foot black plastic lettering we had, in a moment of blind optimism, stuck to the track surface. The idea had been to film a shot for the title sequence, but when at one point there were six of us crouching on the ground in the rain and hail trying to keep the sticky letters onto the wet concrete surface long enough to film the shot, we were beginning to question our sanity. It was altogether a miserable day. The only thing that saved it was Graeme - he never once lost his sense-of-humour or his patience - indeed when things reached an all-time low and we were ready to pack-up and go home in the rain, it was he who persuaded us all to stay and wait out the storm. I think it must be the only time in the BBC's history that a film crew has been persuaded to stay on location by a contributor, and certainly the first time when the contributor was the world's number one pursuit cyclist. Graeme, thank you! R.D.

... but his endless enthusiasm kept the film crew going.

THE FUTURE'S IN THE FRIDGE

"Chocolate, chocolate and more chocolate... Just a few bars today because I'm not very peckish"

Colin Jackson, World champion, Commonwealth and
World record holder, 110m hurdles

C olin Jackson and Linford Christie are both World champions. They excel over sprint distances, from 60 metres, up to an extended 200 metres for Christie. They share the same manager and are, in fact, partners in many off-track ventures. The main difference between them is that one runs flat and the other negotiates hurdles. That, and their diets.

That they prefer alternative nourishment is not explained satisfactorily by the different requirements of their respective disciplines. Although Jackson has to hurdle, he must also prepare to match Christie's speed, between obstacles. He is the 60 metre European indoor sprint champion in his own right (albeit in the absence of Christie). The contrast in diets mirrors a contrast in temperament and lifestyles. These two factors are, largely speaking, the main influence in what we eat. Away from the track, athletes are, after all, only human.

Christie, the methodical performer, eats regularly. He makes time for meals and he eats well. Such discipline, all year round, competing or otherwise, gives him an edge. That is important to the ultimate competitor. He sulks when he is hungry. He sometimes cannot speak with the irritation it causes him. His body has very little fat which is consequence of a diet that would win him top marks with most nutritionists.

Jackson, the restless live wire, frequently forgets to eat. Out of season, he would pick up the wooden spoon award from the nutritionist so impressed with Christie's consumption. What's more, he would use it to shovel a dietician's nightmare down his throat. He loves junk food, and lots of it. During the season he eats concentrated protein and chocolate; again, lots of it. On race days, he has coffee and cake for

Stuttgart 1993. Colin Jackson becomes the fastest hurdler of all time.

breakfast, and even more chocolate. After running, he eats lettuce. He hates fruit and loves sweets.

Christie maintains that the pair never argue over food because neither likes what the other eats. Jackson agrees: "If there was a table, half covered with doughnuts, sweets, cream cakes, and pizza, and the other half with fish, grapes, some bananas, juice, and the like, Linford would not touch the sweet side and I wouldn't touch the other side. There would be no argument. We'd just walk up and take what we both wanted."

One man's meat is another man's poison. Substitute fruit and sweets in the old adage and you have some sort of an explanation for why two top athletes, performing in disciplines that require many similar qualities, adopt radically different approaches to diets. A lot of decisions about diet are based on finding a formula that an athlete is happy with. Not much science in that, more human nature. Maybe, after all, you aren't what you eat? Perhaps diet is an irrelevance in athletics. The future's not even in the kitchen, let alone the fridge.

If it isn't, then many athletes today are wasting a lot of time looking for it there. They're depriving themselves of a good old "greasy spoon" in the process, too. A large number of top competitors see diet as an area in which they can make substantial gains on rivals, many of whom see meals as an escape from the discipline of training.

When Sally Gunnell mounted the winner's rostrum in the 1992 Olympic Games, she reached what is the pinnacle for most athletes. But although that day in Barcelona proved, beyond all reasonable doubt, that Gunnell was the world's best 400 metre hurdler, she rejected complacency. She wanted to improve. She decided afterwards that a reassessment of her diet offered her the best chance of enhancing her performance to the extent that it would account for any advances her rivals might manage between Barcelona and the following year's World Championships in Stuttgart.

Out went impurities and in came vegetables. No tea or coffee, only pure water, no processed food, simple sugars, fresh, natural foods and herbal teas. The old Sally

Keen cooks, close friends and frequent training partners — the world's two top sprint athletes share no similarities as far as diet is concerned.

Gunnell "loved biscuits, and would "snack on crisps" after training. Now she feels "light headed" after coffee and gets "all her energy from main meals". There's only the odd hamburger to "stay sane".

Gunnell might argue that proof of her particular pudding is, so to speak, in the eating. She won the World Championship and broke the world record on the back of her abstinence from a good brew. If you are unconvinced that diet is important to athletes, then the World Championship gold medal for 400 metres hurdles is pretty persuasive evidence to the contrary. Equally, Gunnell's search for "organic vitamins" could suggest that athletes can become a tad obsessive about the importance of what you eat. Red herrings for breakfast? Certainly in some cases.

Whether or not an athlete's diet is anything more than culinary psychology, their motivation to eat sensibly is different to what compels the majority of the western world's population to monitor its intake. For the latter group, diet usually means deprivation; thousands battle to keep their weight down and consequently eat less, or certainly try to. When the scales tip to their satisfaction the aim becomes to maintain the new equilibrium. Translated, this usually means eating "better".

A few, much envied by those most seriously afflicted by vanity, have to eat to keep their weight up. They are encouraged to eat protein and other weight-enhancing compounds and can do so oblivious to the usual consequences. The ability to "eat anything" and remain unaffected around the middle is much coveted. To most, these people represent a lucky minority.

In athletics, the mirror and the scales are largely an irrelevance. What's more important to the likes of Jackson is the power to weight ratio. He needs power to go faster between the hurdles, but he also has to shift his frame over the obstacles. In the winter he tries to put on weight to sustain him during hard pre-season training and then lose it over the course of the season. He loses up to five pounds in weight in the summer as his frame goes from seven per cent body fat to five per cent through a tough

'We are here. We are The Contenders!'

'no fat' diet. As he sheds the pounds, what remains is pure muscle. This weight loss improves his power to weight ratio.

Absolute weight levels are important only in a handful of disciplines where it would be unfair if opponents differed significantly in mass - judo, weightlifting, and, of course, boxing. This presents an altogether more sophisticated challenge to the competitor: achieving a satisfactory power to weight ratio when the weight half of the equation has already been fixed by competition rules. For them, diet is crucial.

One of Britain's most promising boxers, Danny Williams faces such a challenge. He aims to achieve recognition in Olympic, World and Commonwealth contests as an amateur before graduating to the more competitive professional ranks. There, he will be rewarded with money and championship belts, instead of medals. For now, though, the medals are important. They are likely to help Williams get established in the much tougher programme when he ceases to be a "gentleman" and becomes a "player": the early purses for a professional are likely to be that much bigger if the promoter can say that their Danny Boy has a Commonwealth gold, to go with a European boxing bronze he won in Turkey in 1993.

Williams never wanted to be a boxer. Family pressure forced him into it at the age of

Through diet and training, Stephen Ward must maximise his power-to-weight ratio. He must be as light as possible without sacrificing his lifting strength.

Having reached the top of the world in her chosen sport, Sally Gunnell is now looking to make further advances in her performance by fine-tuning her diet.

11. It took him two years to start to enjoy it and to realise that he was quite good at it, so he decided to carry on. If he does not achieve his ambition of becoming "heavyweight champion of the world" he will, at least, have achieved some public acclaim.

. In a perfect world Williams would not have to sweat about his weight. He would fight in the super heavyweight category where competitors can tip the scales at whatever they feel comfortable at. The sky is the limit. But, although it may be difficult to comprehend for less substantial mortals, Williams, at six foot two inches, is not big enough to fight in a weight category which begins at 91 kg. He would not be strong enough. His frame is competitive in the ring only in the "heavyweight" category, one below this with an upper weight limit of around 14 stone, 5 pounds.

Between competitions, Williams balloons to over 16 stone. Like Colin Jackson, he loves junk food like pizza. His national squad physiologist, Marcus Smith, jokes that he should be sponsored by McDonald's. He despairs that Williams possesses an in-built weakness for fry-ups. Bacon rashers do not feature on the approved list of pre-fight eats.

Williams must lose this excess weight to have any chance of winning a medal. A

In order to draw up a dietary programme to bring him safely down to his fighting weight, boxer Danny Williams' nutritionist must put him through a series of rigorous tests.

normal sized super heavyweight would simply be too strong for him. There can be only one course of action for Williams if he wants to box and win: to change his diet and shed the pounds.

Of course, Williams could lose the stone and a half he needs too quickly. Indeed, most boxers can "weigh in" at anything under a stone of their normal fighting weight, the scales returning to a mark outside the legal guidelines if they eat a substantial meal and drink plenty of fluid once the weigh-in is over. But what is shifted in the sauna, or by frantic, last ditch gym sessions in the days leading up to the fight is known as dead weight. Last minute weight loss is for desperate fighters. Losing weight so rapidly can leave even a strong heavyweight as weak as a kitten after a few rounds - with inevitable consequences. Weight loss has to be achieved without sacrificing strength. A crash diet usually leaves a boxer eating canvas.

Williams achieves his weight loss by a combination of exercise and diet changes over a period of six weeks before his appointments in the ring. He is not losing dead weight. Lose that and he forfeits the fight even before it starts. He needs to burn fat stores, not the pockets of carbohydrates which provide him with energy and which he will need to draw on in competition. Dead weight loss is simply burning up the resources that are needed in competition - short term weight loss means carbohydrate reserves are being depleted, which would leave him weak. It is fat stores that have to go, not strength.

This struggle begins with diet. For starters, pizza is out. The shopping trolley which usually heaves with Italian items turns healthy. The frying pan gathers dust while the cereal bowl features daily in the washing-up pile. The golden rule is "grill not fry". His reward for sticking to his diet is chocolate - but in moderation. When he's not training, Williams can eat three to four Twix a day. In training, the occasional chocolate biscuit is allowed for good behaviour.

A change in his training routine completes the job of shifting around 20 redundant pounds. Marcus Smith, Williams' scientific advisor, aims to help him lose weight but not strength. The plan is to devise an excercise routine that will deplete his stores of excess fat, but leave his carbohydrate reserves intact. These will be his energy reserves when the time comes to fight.

It is an unavoidable fact that the human body will use carbohydrate as a fuel in preference to fat - hence the familiar stubbornness of thighs and tummies to submit to the once weekly work-out and miraculously disappear. However, if exercise is maintained at a certain level for long enough, the body's energy-producing cells will start to burn more fat than they would under normal stress. The art of efficient fat loss is to find that exercise level and make the body work at it: carbohydrates will still be used along with the fat but, with

Danny Williams.
'Everything I enjoy has to go — pizzas, sweets and social life. You can't go on partying when you're supposed to be out running.'

a carefully controlled diet, it can be replaced and fat levels left low. The overall effect ensures high carbohydrate stores and low fat deposits — low weight but good strength.

In order to find that magic exercise threshold, Smith tests Williams' blood for lactate levels while he runs on a treadmill. Lactate is a by-product of the fast burning of carbohydrates — a sure indicator that exercise is too vigorous to be powered by fat. Consequently, the ideal exercise level will be where Williams is working hard, but not so hard his lactate levels start to rise. Once the right pace for weight loss is known, Williams can plan the heavy road mileage schedules that all boxers must endure in the build up for the fight, and know that as he pounds the roads, he is losing weight but not energy — getting leaner AND meaner.

The impact that science has made on traditional boxing training is to provide a margin of error. Where before fighters might have had to shift half a stone or so by sweating out fluids in a sauna the morning before a weigh-in, and then step into the ring dehydrated and 'dead-at-the-weight', they can now effectively manage weight loss over weeks or months. Boxers can still sweat out their last few pounds in the sauna, but through careful re-hydration with salt-rich fluids, they can fight fit and strong. A well planned diet, backed up by the right exercise programme, means that when Williams is in the last round of a fight he should have the reserves that will allow him to battle on for that extra medal winning minute.

The importance of diet to the likes of Williams is difficult to understate. Without care, he loses. In other disciplines, failure is less easy to attribute to a lack of planning in the kitchen. Blame is easily apportioned elsewhere. When unrestrained eating is punished by a boxing glove, so to speak, most take note. Even the sweetest tooth would feel compelled to show some restraint if the consequences of a pig-out involved fighting men with both a height and weight advantage. Danny Williams knows that without discipline in the dining room he would have to step between the ropes to meet physically advantaged super heavyweights. He would probably leave the ring horizontally.

In contrast, Chris Boardman, an Olympic cycle pursuit gold medal winner in Barcelona, believes there is widespread ignorance about the benefits of a diet designed specifically for the needs of his sport. He believes his rivals seriously neglect diet. Now a professional cyclist, he maintains that his diet gives him an edge in a world where seconds are crucial.

Having won gold, Boardman's current aim is to win the Tour de France, the ultimate cycle challenge. The training requirements for the Tour are very different to those he undertook to clinch gold in Spain. The mileage is much greater. He has to complete up to three times as much time on the bike. As a result, Boardman has adopted a new diet that he believes improves his chance of winning.

A traditional cyclist's diet, high in carbohydrates, would be adequate, were Boardman in a position to consume them. In fact, the mileage requirements of Tour cycling are such that there is not enough time in a day for the necessary calorific intake. Of course, cyclists have traditionally resolved this dilemma by refuelling while racing, but there are related problems with consuming solid food while riding. Simply put, it cannot be

converted quickly and efficiently enough into energy.

Just as his great rival Graeme Obree did with training, Boardman broke down the problem into its simplest form: the need to consume an efficient source of energy. The result is that he rejected the glucose drinks that might normally be the first choice for energy replacement, in favour of long chain carbohydrate polymers. Pure glucose is the simplest form of sugar used by the body and would enter the blood stream too quickly. The result would be an immediate sugar 'rush', followed by the body's natural over correction and a longer sugar 'low'. Long chain polymers, however, are more complex forms of sugar: they take a little time to be broken down in the stomach before they release their energy. Therefore there is no sugar surge to upset the body's balance, just · a controlled thrust of power. ▶

Chris Boardman star of the cycling track is now making the change to long distance road races. Performing well is a delicate balancing act between diet and fitness.

Q. How has the extra training for the Tour affected your diet?
CHRIS BOARDMAN: The same principle applies, but it has to be more closely adhered

Long-distance cycling races can last up to seven hours a day. This presents a problem: the competitors do not have enough time _off_ the bike to consume all the calories that they will need _on_ the bike the following day.

to, to make sure that I get the amount of calories that I need, which can be up to 9000 calories in a day. It's virtually physically impossible to eat that amount. That's the biggest problem. Your calorie expenditure is higher and you need to put more calories back, but you have less time to do it because you spend more time riding a bike. We have to eat on a bike. The best way to do it is to eat in a liquid form using blue page polymers. It starts to get into the system within three minutes, and, because it's a long chain start molecule, it doesn't actually give you the problems with insulin that simple sugars will give. It's probably one of the biggest steps forward, in sports nutrition in the last decade. In fact, I'm sure it is.

Isn't it really boring?
Yes! It's a bland taste and you are not actually eating anything. You're sitting there for four to seven hours just drinking the same stuff day in, day out, you're not looking forward to a cereal bar or a banana or something to break the monotony. You've go to be convinced about it to make yourself do it.

■ Like Sally Gunnell, Boardman believes that his diet can make the difference between first and second place. That his rivals, particularly the French, whose enthusiasm for cycling far exceeds the frequently apathetic attitude of the British public towards the discipline, largely ignore the innovations of the last decade, is something he hopes to capitalise on.

For Boardman, eating is just another aspect of training, requiring discipline and scientific precision. It is unlikely that you will find him tucking into what just happened to be in the fridge. Each meal has a purpose; to make him go faster for longer. ▶

Q. Does everyone else believe in the effectiveness of your diet?
CHRIS BOARDMAN: No, they don't, which is great for me, because it means I have an advantage. In Europe, they're much more traditional. They've never really looked into it. We did because the papers that have been published on it showed it produced a significant improvement.

Is there an "old guard" attitude towards eating?
Very much so. If you go to France, they say, "This is the way we've always done it, food is food and water's water, and you don't mix the two up". A lot have been around for a very long time and find it difficult to accept new ideas.

What are the specific benefits to you of the diet?
The biggest advantage is probably immediately after training. The carbohydrate goes

Chris Boardman takes a scientific approach to all his training. To him what he eats is as important as the design of the bike he rides.

into the system quicker in the first hour after training, so if you drink it then you've started your recuperation immediately so the next day, or whenever, you can train again and harder.

Do you count calories?
Yes, I have a 2,400-calorie-a-day allowance and, on top of that, I can have another 1,300 calories a day for each hour of full training. The problem is that the calorie demand for a day may exceed 9,000 calories which is virtually physically impossible to eat unless you're, perhaps, eating pure lard. It has to be spread out over a couple of days.

Do you analyse all your food?
You've got to look at the constituent parts very carefully. I have a computer programme that analyses any food, from sushi to sponge cake. It's a bit like learning a new language I suppose, and you just find your way around the food chain. I'm very careful to get a good range of protein, fish, chicken and lamb, and I tend not to eat too much red meat. I stick to the simple foods, breads, pastas and rice, for the carbohydrates. It's a bit boring and not much fun, but nowadays we've got such a health conscious nation you can go out and get three per cent fat chips!

"Chocolate, chocolate and more chocolate. . ."

■ The mention of junk food brings Colin Jackson back into focus. He shares with Boardman a belief in concentrated food stuffs as a source of energy. This is not through necessity, though. After all, Jackson's discipline has a duration of seconds rather than the hours in competition Boardman spends. It's because Jackson, very much one of the new breed of switched-on athletes, believes in taking advantage of every new development.

In pre-season training, and during a summer of intense competition, Jackson supplements his usual diet with chocolate and Creatine. He started eating the former on the advice of his friend and rival Canadian hurdler Mark McKoy who learnt that many successful Eastern European competitors ate up to 200 grams of milk chocolate the night before the big event for its controlled release of sugar and caffeine. Jackson does not particularly like chocolate. It was his respect for the Eastern Europeans that compelled him to put aside his aversion to it.

Few share Jackson's distaste for one of life's luxuries. About the same number, perhaps, who understand the

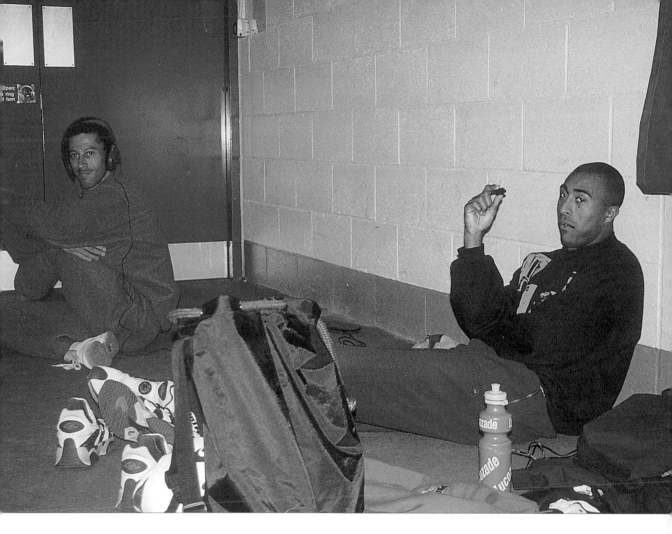

other aspect of his track season diet, Creatine. Like many other modern sprinters, Jackson takes this natural substance usually found in red meat, in a concentrated tablet form. In the body, Creatine is a raw form of muscle fuel and high levels of it allow the body's efficient and explosive energy system to work for fractions of a second longer. In a sport where those fractions frequently make the difference between first and second place, Creatine can help you win. The consumption of such a substance is not illegal, but neither is it particularly pleasant. Like chocolate, it is something Jackson endures in the pursuit of medals and records.

Substances like Creatine are, however, the source of much controversy. A bi-product of the advances made in diet that have made Creatine available and affordable, is the moral question about whether athletes should seek to enhance their performance by any means within the rules. Some argue substances like it go against the spirit of the sport. How natural is a product that is massively concentrated and processed? Some say that it should be banned.

One of the difficulties in deciding what should happen with many such 'food supplements' is that they often occur naturally in the body all the time. Everybody has a certain amount of Creatine in their system. All that Jackson and others are doing is to boost their levels just before a race. However, competition in sport is supposed to be

Sometime dietary adviser Mark McKoy sits back as Colin Jackson prepares for a race.

between athletes and not the tools that they are given. It could be argued that, since sprinters from Zaire are unlikely to have access to concentrated Creatine, it is unfair and should be banned. But does this mean that concentrated vitamins and energy drinks should be banned too?

Clearly the moral question is difficult to answer. Fortunately for athletes it is also an irrelevance: what matters is not whether it is 'right' to use a substance, but whether it is legal according to the codes drawn up by the sport's governing body. The moral question then shifts to those who advise the governing bodies. That it is still a difficult problem to come to grips with is clear from the unease with which Dr Ron Maughan, Chairman of the British Olympic Association's nutritional committee, weighs up the rights and wrongs of an athlete's single-minded pursuit of track glory. ▶

Q. What exactly is Creatine?

RON MAUGHAN: It's a normal dietary component, which is present in meat. When we eat meat we eat Creatine. It's used in the body in a variety of different ways. Primarily it's used in the energy-producing systems of muscle, particularly when the muscle does high-intensity exercise. Creatine phosphate is a compound that's used in energy transfer within the cell, so we need Creatine to achieve high-intensity exercise. When we take very large amounts of Creatine phosphate in the muscle, it acts partly as an energy store. When we need energy very rapidly, the Creatine phosphate's broken down and is used to produce ATP, and that ATP makes the muscles work. If we can't produce ATP fast enough, we can't do high-intensity exercise.

How much do you have to take for it to affect your performance?
You'd have to eat, perhaps, 20 or 30 steaks or their equivalent in a day, very large amounts compared with what's normally in the diet.

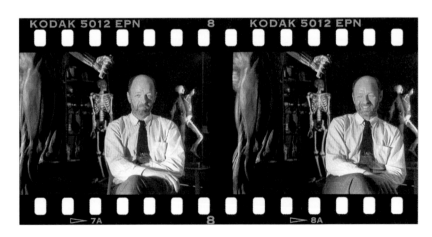

Dr Ron Maughan, Chairman of the British Olympic Association's Nutritional Committee advises athletes on how to achieve their potential through controlling their diet.

Colin Jackson is convinced that the food supplement, Creatine enables him to make minute but vital improvements to his performances.

In what forms can you take it so that you eat the equivalent?
If you purify Creatine, it's just a white powder, so you can take it in tablet form, or you can dissolve it in a drink.

Does this make it a food, a drink, or a drug?
It's a very difficult area, to know whether doing this makes Creatine a food, because it's a normal food component, or whether it makes it a drug, because the amounts that you can take by using it in a purified form are far greater than you could ever get from your diet.

If it can be argued that it is a drug, does this raise a moral issue?
If you ask me, philosophically, then I would say, I think, perhaps, it's wrong to take such a highly purified compound, with the specific aim of improving performance, but if you're an athlete, a sprinter, and you say to me, should I take Creatine, I say "Is it on the banned list?" If it isn't, it then depends on whether you want to win or not. If you're competing in the Olympics, and the other guys are just as talented as you, just as motivated, what's going to make the difference? Maybe taking that Creatine's going to make the difference so you've got no choice if you're competing at the top level: you have to take it.

Are purified food components drugs?
There are always debates about food components which you extract and purify. If we take something like caffeine, for example, it's a normal food component, but you can purify it and then take it in very large amounts. Is it then a food? Many people would say,

no, when you do that it acts as a drug. If you take some of the individual Amino Acids, you can purify those and take very large amounts, and they can affect some of the body's functioning. With some of those compounds, they act on the brain, and then we say that's a drug. The balance is very, very fine, it's very difficult to come down very strongly one way or the other, this is a food, that's a drug.

What about vitamins?
Many athletes take very large amounts of vitamins. These very large amounts mostly are not harmful, so there's no risk involved, it just wastes the athlete's money, and if the athlete wants to do that, that's fine. I don't think there's the same concern because most of the vitamins are not effective in improving performance.

■ The banned list does, at least, provide a workable framework for athletes. But Dr Maughan maintains that it is unrealistic to expect any more from it than that. ▶

Q. What purpose does the banned list serve?
RON MAUGHAN: The list of banned substances is there to remove the moral debate for athletes. If it's on the list, it's wrong. And a decision has been made by those best able to come to that decision, the medical authorities, who know what the risks and benefits of different substances are. They've looked at all these things and they have said these substances are banned. And that removes the moral debate for the athletes. Someone else has had that argument.

In all sports dehydration is a very real danger and specialized sports drinks can make a major contribution to an athlete's performance. For Chris Boardman they have the further advantage of enabling him to feed whilst on the bike.

What is the main rationale for what goes on the list and what doesn't?

The most important consideration for the medical commission is, will it damage an athlete's health? If it's a substance which athletes take because it improves performance and there is any risk to health then it's banned and quite rightly so. That's the main consideration at the end of the day.

■ Wrestling with morality is thirsty work. If athletes are unable to decide for themselves one way or the other, they are at least well advised to avoid getting dehydrated in the process, even if the lower-profile nuances of fluid intake provoke a less passionate debate than solids do. Yvonne Murray is a rarity in that she is someone who is prepared to go to great lengths to avoid the threat of dehydration; the skip load of Highland Spring water that she had shipped out to South Africa where she was training bears testimony to that.

Murray's concern is shared away from the track. Governments have spent considerable resources exploring the military connotations of dehydration. The American government undertook research into whether a soldier deprived of water in heat will, in time, become less in need of fluid intake. On concluding that this was not the case, much research was conducted into finding the best way to keep soldiers adequately watered in combat situations like the recent Gulf War.

Athletics remains way behind the warlords in this respect. Unfortunately, one of the main problems of ensuring that you are taking adequate fluid when training and competing is that by the time the mind registers thirst, the body has lost enough fluid to impair performance. And by then it is too late. The body is much better at sending messages that it is hungry.

On the modern athletics roundabout, the consequences of this, according to Dr Maughan, are difficult to overstate. News of dehydration may arrive belatedly, but the consequences are of immediate concern. ▶

Q. How big a concern is dehydration?
RON MAUGHAN: Dehydration is a big problem for athletes these days because most of the major events are held somewhere hot. It makes good television so they have the event in Barcelona, in Tokyo, in Atlanta. It's not so good for the athletes because it causes dehydration and that affects performance. Add this to the fact that the athlete also has the problem of competing to the highest level at the major championships. We need to look at the problems of competing in the heat, the problems of training in the heat, the problems of adaptation to the heat and also how to help the athlete before and during competition.

Does this give an unfair advantage to the athletes who are used to such conditions?
It's a bit like altitude. People who are born and raised at altitude have an advantage over those at sea level in events run at high altitude. If we have events in the heat then people who live in hot climates almost certainly have a significant advantage over those who live in cold climates. But it's a fact of life there's no point in complaining. The wider issue is the fact that when you look at how much is at stake, the athletes often seem remarkably unaware of some of the realities. The difference in winning and losing is increasingly small. If you are suffering from dehydration the chances are you are going to lose. But when we speak to many of the competitors they don't have a clear understanding of what they should be doing.

Is dehydration important all the time?
Dehydration is a huge issue. Where it becomes most obvious is in endurance events and the prime example is marathon running. Think about the famous collapses in marathon running; there's Dorando Pietri in the Olympics Marathon in 1908 who collapsed and was helped across the line and disqualified, Jim Peters - during the Commonwealth Games in 1954 who collapsed after staggering into the stadium, the Swiss lady, Gabriel Andersson-Shiess, at the Los Angeles Olympics who staggered across the line in the stadium. Those people were all competing in very hot climates, which they weren't used to and they had major problems. The endurance athletes are aware of the problems of dehydration, but many of the other athletes are not. If we speak to the sprinters, they say dehydration is not a problem because they only run for ten seconds or 15 seconds, but of course they train for a couple of hours a day when they go somewhere hot and all the time they're dehydrated. The swimmers say they're in the swimming pool so we shouldn't be dehydrated, but they are sweating all the time and it's a real problem. Look at the games

in Barcelona, for example. There was no air conditioning in the athletes' village. So many people said: "Well I'm not doing much training in a couple of days before competition, so I don't need to worry too much about dehydration", but you're sweating the whole time. And the sweat losses are very substantial. And if they're not replaced you don't perform well.

What evidence is there that dehydration is important?
We have studies showing that if you raise the temperature and make people sweat more then performance goes down. In hot climates your ability to exercise is drastically reduced and there is also a risk to health if you become seriously dehydrated and over-heated. Some coaches still have the idea that you can adapt to dehydration. They believe that if you don't drink in training, you'll perform better when it comes to competition where the opportunities of drinking are restricted. In the same way marathon runners used to look on drinking as a sign of weakness - "I made it to 22 miles without taking a drink so I had a good day" - but that is absolute nonsense.

Are athletes being educated in the problems?
We have to encourage the athletes to drink in training because it has so many benefits benefits. Firstly, the quality of the training session is improved because they can exercise hard and improvements in performance come with hard training. Secondly, if we get the athletes to drink during training then they know what to do in competition. We see athletes who never drink in training go to the Olympics and expect to drink in the final but they don't know what drink to take, they don't know how much, they find that they've got something they don't like the taste of. And then we have a big problem.

■ Chris Boardman is an exception to your average ignorant athlete. A clear spin off from his diet is that it helps him combat dehydration. ▶

Q. How important is fluid intake?
CHRIS BOARDMAN: Fluid is the most important thing. Your performance will drop off a lot more rapidly from lack of fluid than it will from lack of calories. It's something that has to be addressed very carefully. It's also one of the things that most people neglect in a race situation. I have looked at a person's bike in the past, seen they've got two bottles, and after two hours only a couple of sips have gone. In a training ride of five hours on a reasonably warm day, you can get through four pints of liquid no problem and still lose over 2 kg in weight.

How much fluid do you have to lose before your performance starts to drop off?
Something like two per cent of body weight from fluid loss will significantly affect performance. One of the pluses of glucose polymer is that, because you are feeding in a liquid form from the bottle, you're addressing the two most important problems in one

go. When you are in a race, unwrapping some food and chewing it is a bit of a problem, whereas just grabbing a bottle and taking a couple of sips is less of a problem. So you can address the energy problem and dehydration at the same time.

■ It must disappoint the manufacturers of the plethora of leisure drinks on the market that Boardman is, in fact, one of only a few enlightened members of the sports fraternity. Many of his fellow performers from other walks of sport sadly fail to acknowledge the importance of drinking correctly. Dr Maughan vividly recalls the sight of Jennifer Carpriati, the top US tennis player, puzzling over her next move in preparing a re-hydrating concoction at a crucial point in a third and deciding set of an important match at Wimbledon. Faced with the drink in powder form, Miss Capriati was summoned back to court by the umpire before she had concluded that her nutritionist's specially prepared package needed the addition of some water for it to assist her in overcoming a particularly tough opponent. Mercifully, she rejected the option of consuming the undiluted powder, an act which would surely have made her feel worse and may have ultimately cost her the match.

Cynics of marketing will be disappointed in Dr Maughan's view that many of the sporting drinks on the market offer real assistance to athletes in staving off dehydration and its damaging consequences. Dr Maughan believes that many of the sports drinks formulae have a sound scientific base, although mixed along with the aggressive advertising hype that exploits the youth's dependency on guidance from role models, they often leave a sour taste in the mouth.

This advance, uncomplicated by any morality debate, is a cause for celebration. If athletes feel inclined to toast the work of sports drink companies throughout the world, they should not shy away from a shandy, either.

Although breweries may be surprised to learn that they have a role to play in helping athletes to gold medals and new records, Dr Maughan argues that beer may indeed be of use to athletes during training and in competition itself as well as in enhancing post-race victory celebrations or in soothing the pain of defeat. ▶

Q. Are athletes knowledgeable about the effectiveness of sports drinks, and even beer?
RON MAUGHAN: Well, we're working very hard to try and make them knowledgeable but it's obvious that some of them don't know, and there are those who still believe that plain water is best, in spite of the evidence that taking the sports drinks helps to improve performance.

Would you ever recommend plain water?
No, I don't think there's any situation when plain water's better than one of the Maughan sports drinks. The sports drinks are formulated to maximise performance. They give water and, because they contain sugar and salt, the water's more readily absorbed in the gut. The sugar acts as an energy source and improves performance. The salts help

Awareness of the advantages of sports drinks is spreading. The Scottish wrestling team are now breaking with tradition in order to drink during training.

replace the losses in sweat and help promote recovery after exercise. Recovery after exercise is very important between competitions and training sessions. After exercise the drinks you take should do several things; they should replace the energy you've lost and the glucose helps to do that, and you should replace the water and the salts help to retain it. If you drink plain water the kidneys are very effective at getting rid of it. And when you've lost sweat you've lost water and salts. You need to replace those salts in order to retain the water that you've lost.

Does the salt in the water not make it taste horrible?
There's a big industry that's grown up around these sports drinks and they've made a reasonable job of making these things taste pretty good. Because you have to add quite a lot of salt to these drinks to get the biggest benefit, the drinks taste quite salty, and you

have to mask that taste. If they don't taste good, people won't drink them and of course the industry know that. But, you have to remember that when you're hot and sweaty things that are salty taste much better than they usually do. If you try out a sports drink you should always do so in the situation where you're going to drink it. When you're sitting comfortably in your chair at home, it probably tastes a bit on the salty side. But when you've been out training for the afternoon you're hot and sweaty it'll probably taste a lot different, and a lot better.

Does your body know when it's lacking in water?
No. One of the big problems is that you don't become thirsty until after you're already dehydrated, and, from a performance point of view, that's too late. Your performance is already down before you're thirsty.

So you've got to force yourself to drink?
You have to practice in training. You have to recognise the signals of dehydration. You have to know that you will become dehydrated, so you drink before hand to prevent it happening. If you wait until it's too late and you're actually dehydrated, you're going to lose.

Is that hard work?

You can learn with practice how to do it. But one thing you can't do is drink huge amounts of plain water. If you ever try drinking a couple of pints of water you just can't do it. You can drink a couple of pints of some of the other drinks, and you can mix and match, but water is very difficult to drink large volumes of. What you can drink of course is large amounts of beer! There's actually a real possibility that drinking beer shandy might be beneficial, and it's something that the athletes themselves - particularly some of the games players - have recognised. If you're very dehydrated and you've lost several litres of fluid it's very difficult to drink enough, but two or three pints probably does no harm so long as it's *after* rather than *before*. It seems to be possible to drink three, four, five pints of beer shandy. You couldn't imagine drinking five pints of water after a game of rugby. It's just not physically possible to drink five pints of water or five pints of coke. There's no way you could drink that amount. The body's got very good mechanisms for preventing that from happening, and one of the things the salt in the drink does is allow us to continue drinking.

■ Linford Christie may take some convincing about the beer. It is a long time since the Olympic and World Champion enjoyed a couple of rum and blackcurrants with some of his

Colin Jackson controls his diet rigorously throughout the year. In the winter he aims to increase his weight to develop his power over the flat and, as he prepares to race in the summer, a strict 'no fat' diet maintains his strength whilst reducing the mass he will have to carry over the barriers.

JACKSON FISH STEW (LOW FAT)
Ingredients:
seafood flakes
spring onions, chopped
4 large mushrooms, cut coarsely
chives
pepper
fat-free Milk
rice
frozen peas
saffron
stock Cubes

Instructions
Instead of seafood flakes you can use other fish - we used cod and prawns. Be careful though, not all fish is low fat. Beware of salmon and haddock.

Start the rice as this takes longest. Wash the rich thoroughly to remove starch, and put into pan with equal amount of water. Add the saffron, stock cubes and peas. When the rice begins to simmer put on the lid. The rice is done when it absorbs all the water.

Chop the chives, spring onion, mushrooms. Add these and the fish to the fat-free milk and bring to the boil. Do not let it boil vigorously. After about 20 minutes the dish is done, and ready to eat. Serve with rice. Add pepper to taste.

LINFORD'S BREAD AND BUTTER PUDDING
Ingredients
8 slices of white bread
2 oz butter
4 oz sultanas
2 oz caster sugar
2 large eggs
3/4 of a pint of milk
3 oz coconut
cinnamon or nutmeg to taste

Instructions
Tear the slices of bread into small pieces and put into a two pint oven-proof dish. Add the milk and let it stand for ten minutes, so the bread can soak up the milk. Using a fork, mash the bread completely into the milk. Sprinkle the sultanas and coconut over the mixture. Mix well. Melt the margarine gently in a saucepan over a low heat, add the sugar and remove from heat. Add to pudding and mix well. Beat two eggs and fold into mixture. Sprinkle with spice to taste. Cook at gas mark 4 (180C, 350F) for 55 minutes. Pierce pudding with knife. It is ready when the knife comes out clean.

SALLY GUNNELL'S STIR FRY

Ingredients
2 free range chicken breasts
1 large carrot
1 green pepper
1 large courgette
125g of mushrooms
(All the vegetables Sally uses are organically grown)
250g of wholemeal pasta
oilseed rape oil
1 chicken oxo cube
soy sauce to taste

Instructions
Chop the vegetables roughly. Cut the chicken breasts into bite-sized chunks.

Put about 2 tablespoonfuls of rape oil into a wok and heat it gently on a low heat, add the chicken when the oil is hot enough to make it sizzle. Cook, stirring constantly for about ten minutes until it has lost its pinkness. Meanwhile put the pasta in a pan of boiling water and simmer until tender. This will take approximately ten minutes, but see the packet for the exact time - it will vary with the pasta used.

Crunch up the Oxo cube and add this to the chicken. Then add the vegetables to the wok and stir until they're lightly cooked to taste. Shake Soy Sauce over to taste.

Finally drain the pasta and add it to the ready-to-serve stir fry.

THE MAIN CONTENDERS

COLIN JACKSON
Date of Birth: 18 February 1967
Height: 5' 11 ¹/₂" / 1.82 m
Weight: 11st 9lbs / 74 kg

COMPETITION RECORD:
110m Hurdles: 1993 World champion (and world record holder);
1993, 1991, 1989 European Cup champion;
1992 World Cup champion;
1990 European champion;
1990 Commonwealth champion;
1989 World Cup silver;
1988 Olympic silver;
1987 European Cup silver;
1987 World Championship bronze;
1986 Commonwealth silver.

60m Sprint: 1994 European Indoor champion.
60m Hurdles: 1994, 1989 European Indoor champion.

old West London track friends. Now, the supreme track disciplinarian prefers not to drink.

But thirst can be a powerful thing. On an occasion in Australia, Christie's need to counteract a post-training session dryness compelled him to drink the only bottle in the fridge on his return to his lodgings. Unfortunately, it was cider. Christie maintains it was only a small bottle and that he drank less than half of it. No matter. The soon-to-be Olympic gold medal and World Championship winner quickly found himself as wobbly as a marathon runner entering the stadium.

The emotions Christie experienced, fortified by his chosen tipple, were those of the winning athlete. He remembers feeling emotional and overwhelmed by the successful completion of a run-of-the-mill session. Only the presence of Dalton Grant, one of Britain's top high-jumpers prompted him to get a grip. The subsequent ribbing that would have followed if he had let on what was going on inside his head was a sobering thought.

. Many a Friday night drinker, similarly affected, has claimed "it was only a tiny bottle" and that they "did not even have half". Christie laughs heartily at the memory of what he maintains was a "trap", but his experiences highlight how the impact of dehydration can be underestimated by even the most disciplined track star. Weak from loss of fluid, Christie did not need much cider for it to take effect.

The impact of diet may not be as immediate, but the effect of neglect should not be underestimated, either. Of course, there are good grounds for arguing that much of the debate about diet is debate about general health and well-being; an athlete happy with his or her diet is likely to run faster than one who exists on a diet of scientifically concocted gruel. The psychologically beneficial effects to the disciplined performer of occasionally "pigging out" may more than cancel out any damage from the consumption of unnutritional fare.

The compelling exception to this argument is with cases where weight restrictions are placed on performers, like boxers and weightlifters. They have to operate within set parameters and, as a result, must pay close attention to their diet at all times. Unless, that is, the boxer is happy to step in the ring with the super heavyweights and pay the consequences of a traditional English breakfast. In such circumstances, the pig is not the only loser when a contender opts for an extra rasher of bacon. Food for thought.

Filming Colin Jackson

It is often said that Linford Christie is the King of the track. If this is so, then Colin Jackson, his friend and business partner, is certainly the Prince of Athletics. His grace and beauty over the 3' 6" barriers he faces in his chosen event is matched perfectly by his eloquent and charming manner away from the field of contest. We hoped, during the many fly-on-the-wall filming sessions we had done with the pair that we had amply demonstrated the latter, but capturing the former in a new and electrifying way was one of the greatest challenges of the series.

We had decided that we wanted the viewers to feel like they were running along with Colin as he hurdled, looking directly back at him as his body collapses and expands over the fences. There were two big problems to overcome: the first was to find a vehicle fast enough and controllable enough to keep up with him (a sprinter

FILMING COLIN JACKSON

accelerates over the first few metres faster that a Porsche, and Colin is one of the fastest starters in the world), and the second was to attach the camera to the vehicle in such a way that it could be suspended above the hurdles directly in front of the runner without either knocking the fences over, or distracting the approaching athlete. From my previous experience (I once had to transmit live pictures from the business end of an eight kilometre hole in the ground that was to become the Channel Tunnel) I knew that filming the unusual and uncontrollable was the province of the BBC's Outside Broadcast team. But even they were at a loss as to what to do when we approached them. Through a combination of guess-work and experimentation, we came up with a combination we hoped would work: we had a four-wheeled fat-tyred motorcycle with two backward facing seats on the rear, onto one of which was fixed a six-foot counterweighted arm that could swing out perpendicular to the bike and carry the camera directly in front of the hurdler. We also designed and made some specially adapted hurdles with only one support. We planned to be able to track the camera beneath the barriers as Colin was hurdling over them, thus getting a really unique view of the action of his body. All together, the bike and the ungainly one-legged fences made a somewhat Heath Robinson-like spectacle, but as we arrived very early on a sunny morning at Colin's home track in Cardiff, we hoped they would do the trick.

Paul Grey, Colin's friend and training partner, helped us by standing in for Colin as we rehearsed to see if everything would go smoothly and, eventually, after a few hours of ironing the wrinkles out, we set out for a take. I don't think I have ever seen a more cumbersome piece of film equipment lumber across an athletics track, but the results it produced were better than we had ever hoped: we are proud to say we filmed the finest sprint hurdler of all time, at the peak of his powers, and we think we produced some of the most stunning sports photography ever seen. R.D.

In order to keep up with Colin Jackson to film these pictures we had to create the Heath Robinson-like contraption (overleaf). For the shots on page 72 we needed a shop's security mirror!

FILMING CHRIS BOARDMAN

Chris Boardman is Olympic pursuit cycling champion at 4000m. Last year he turned professional for the French racing team 'Gan' and is now riding road races: instead of 4 minutes on the track, he is racing 6 or 7 hours across the French countryside.

When we came to film Chris we decided the only place to do it was on his bike on the road; as he said to us, "The track's important, but it's only 1% of my time - 99% of it is spent out here, putting in the hours."

Having made that choice, we then had to work out the logistics. The normal way to film a cyclist is from a car - the camera peering through the sun-roof or leaning precariously out of the window. But we wanted something different; we wanted to feel that we weren't just watching the cyclists, but that we were one of them - in amongst the pack, riding the twists and pot-holes just as they were.

We decided that the only way to film their world was to be in it ourselves - on two wheels, camera perched on the back of a motorbike. Mick, our motorcycle pilot, was a veteran of the London Marathon, the Kellogg's Tour of Britain and the Milk Race, and Chris, the cameraman, had spent more days in vehicles of one sort or another seeing the world disappear through a viewfinder than he cared to remember.

The main problem was communications. I had to be able to instruct the cameraman, hear what the cyclists were saying, and be able to talk to Peter Georgi, who was going to be asking the questions. On top of that, where was Pete himself going to be? With the cameraman already on the back of the motorbike there was no room for him there and another motorbike would have been too noisy and cumbersome...

In true producer fashion, I asked Peter Georgi to sort things out.

When I arrived to film, on a miserable February day in Merseyside, I didn't really know what to expect. As it turned out, I need not have worried, Pete had done exactly what was needed. To record Chris Boardman's sound there were microphones hidden on the front of his cycling top and the signal was being radioed to a car up ahead. Both Mick, the pilot, and Chris, the cameraman, were on two way radio walkie-talkies, and Pete had solved the problem of where he was going to be by resurrecting his old racing cycle: in his youth, he assured me, he had been an

Filming an interview on a bike sounds very simple, but filming Chris Boardman was a lot more difficult than any of us imagined.

FILMING CHRIS BOARDMAN

international cyclist himself.

In the end we spent a morning going up and down a 2-mile stretch of wet and windy road, and in his natural environment, on his home roads in the Wirral, we felt we got as close to the real Chris Boardman as it was possible to get. In the cold and damp, everyone worked hard, but the cameraman excelled himself: it is hard to describe exactly what he did, but anyone who has seen a man, no longer in the full flush of youth, standing upright on the pillion of a motorbike, facing backwards and holding a ten kilo camera above his head, will know exactly what I mean. The only person who came away at the end of the day with regrets was Peter Georgi: his legs, he tells me, have never been the same since. R.D.

THE GREY LINE – BANNED SUBSTANCES

Athletes have always taken exotic foods and drugs to try and boost their performances. Everything from turtle blood to the flowers of wild orchids. Some work, some don't make a difference, and some are dangerous. It was because of the abuse of dangerous substances that rules were brought for international competition, banning certain substances. Testing procedures and threshold levels for some compounds were established. To an extent, the line that is drawn between what is acceptable and disqualification is arbitrary. Concentrated food stuffs are the source of controversy. How do you decide whether a substance is a food or a drug? Caffeine is found in coffee, but it can also be supplied as a drug. What is natural, and what is artificial?

The banned list is laid down by the International Olympic Medical Committee, based in Geneva. Virtually all sporting bodies follow their recommendations.

"We don't know where they're going to draw the line next. Is it going to be minerals? Is it going to be vitamins?' We don't know tomorrow what's going to be on the banned list." Colin Jackson

Drug abuse, which the list aims to control, is common in three forms:
STEROIDS. – These build up the muscles during training, and have been detected, most notoriously in weight lifting. Weightlifting associations have attempted to clean up their act. Since then the winning liftes have dropped in weight significantly.
STIMULANTS. – These are used in speed events.
BLOOD DOPING. – An athlete stores a pint of blood (either their own or someone else's) and, just before competition, injects it back into the bloodstream to increase their stamina.

What's new to the list?
HUMAN GROWTH HORMONE. – This is a hormone that promotes the body's own production of anabolic steroids. Because it is naturally found in the bloodstream, a threshold level was set. If the athlete had a hormone level that exceeded this, it was assumed that the athlete had injected extra amounts illegally.

CAFFEINE. – Many athletes used to take huge quantities of caffeine just before a race. Now there is a threshold roughly the equivalent to drinking 12 medium strong cups of coffee before competition.

What's not on the list that might be added in the near future?
CREATINE. – This is *the* fashionable food supplement at the moment. It is naturally found in very small quantities in most red meat. Now a method has been devised to extract it in huge quantities. It is believed to increase the time maximum muscle effort can be maintained. However, some nutritionists have reservations...

"I think it won't be long before Creatine is banned. It gives the athletes who can afford it too much an advantage over those who can't." Dr Ron Maughan, British Olympic Association

TOOLS OF
THE TRADE

*"Sport should be about the athlete,
not the technology."*

Steve Backley, Commonwealth and former World record holder, javelin

Britain boasts two of the world's best cyclists. Chris Boardman won pursuit gold in Barcelona in 1992. Graeme Obree held track cycling's "hour" world record - the distance travelled during 60 minutes of uninterrupted effort. Obree first broke the record in 1993 but Boardman took it off him within a week. Obree won it back again in 1994. There hasn't been British rivalry like it since Yates and Doyle in the early 1980s when the former got picked for the Olympics and a furious Doyle turned professional and won the World pursuit championship, jet-propelled by anger. Boardman and Obree, the Linford Christie and Carl Lewis of the boards; the Yates and Doyle of the 1990s.

Boardman and Obree are probably faster than their predecessors. The sport has moved on. Techniques have been refined and equipment has been improved to enhance performance. In absolute terms, Boardman and Obree, also just about put Yates and Doyle in the shade, although such opinions are always open to debate. As with other sports when generations are compared, you just never know. It is one of the joys of athletics.

It would indeed be a sad day if technology eliminated the human element to sport and competition. The tools of the trade provide the basis for individuals to pit their gifts against each other. They facilitate a comparison of the respective merits of two athletes. Gold medals should never be won and lost anywhere other than on the track, unless it is at the training ground, through dedication and determination.

With performers of such calibre wearing the national vest, it is something of a disappointment that analysis of the respective merits of Boardman and Obree's

The combination of a radical body position and a uniquely designed home-built cycle has propelled Graeme Obree from obscurity to his status as the world's top cyclist.

performances focus as much on the bikes they ride as the riders themselves. Boardman's Olympic bike - the Windcheetah - was produced by the car manufacturers, Lotus, and shattered two world speed records in Spain. It was designed specifically for pursuit racing by Mike Burrows. Obree's machine was altogether more bizarre. Some parts of it came from his washing machine. He calls it Old Faithful.

The involvement of one of the most glamorous car manufacturers was a side-show that was always going to divert attention. The ad hoc nature of Obree's bike made mechanical comparisons, at the expense of the rider's talent, inevitable. Equally so, the view held by some commentators, that the pair's achievements were inextricably linked to their machines, filled much air time and column space.

But the nation's interest in the technology involved with the exploits of probably the two best cyclists Britain has ever had waned. The decline in public fascination was enough to prompt Lotus to drop Burrows. After Barcelona his stock had risen to a level that afforded him "guru" status. Less that two years on, Lotus felt confident enough to go on without his help and he is now working for Giant, the Taiwanese bike design and manufacturer and the British cycle industry's most fiery competitor. By this time Obree's bike had been banned for road races on the basis that it was dangerous. Illegal bicycles are less of an attraction.

Obree in the rainbow-striped jersey of a World Champion demonstrates his bike to Chris Boardman. Always interested in innovation that leads to success, Boardman felt compelled to investigate.

Defeated by Obree (left) in the World Pursuit Championships, Boardman (above) needed to find out whether he had been beaten by man or machine. 'Either way I lose. Either the bike's better and I'll have to have one like it — and that doesn't look like cycling — or Graeme's a better athlete and I've got a lot more work to do.'

Lotus' decision was based on the narrowness of the market that exists for Burrows' speciality. It was not worth the company's while employing him. Banning Obree's bike was a pure safety measure. The clamp down on Old Faithful should not be mistaken as an attempt by cycling's governing authority to rescue the sport for the purists and to check the growing influence that technology has in the sport. Obree maintains that the bike is not revolutionary, but merely designed to suit his build. He argues persuasively. Those who believe that the equipment was the real record breaker might care to reflect that the rider set a new hour record, having failed only 24 hours previously to do so. In preparation for a second assault, he woke every few hours during the night to avoid stiffening up. His achievement in setting a new mark was not the effort of an average athlete. He is equally determined in his defence of a two wheeled friend that has served him well and in awarding himself the credit his performances deserves.

Q. What makes "Old Faithful" special?

GRAEME OBREE: It is the design which makes it different. It's not the best put together bike in the world but it's ideal for me and for my body. The basic idea is that the body can rest in a more natural position, similar to the position when you are lying back and pedalling, upside down.

What made you build it?

The problem with me is that I've got reasonably long arms, (maybe I should've been a

Boardman's hi-tech track cycle is eclipsed by Obree's 'Old Faithful' — constructed in his home using parts from a redundant washing machine.

swimmer instead) and I've always wanted to put my handle bars as low as they would possibly go on a small frame. It looked hideous to a normal person but with my long arms it is ideal. I realised this the very first time I cycled but it wasn't for a few years that I actually realised that the bar across the top of the bicycle was in the way for me. When I realised that this was the case the best thing to do was to remove that tube but obviously a normal bicycle would just fold in half. I did nothing else about it, until a couple of years ago when I thought of a bike with only a single bar which allowed the knees to be closer together. Then I thought of the idea of actually narrowing the bracket down as well . I did a bit of running and looked at cross-country runners. I noticed that their feet almost come together; the natural position for running was the ankles almost touching each other. Cycling's got this six inch gap between the legs for the chain and everything, which is unnatural. I thought, is there any way I could narrow that down to test the theory? I shut my eyes to see where the feet would go, and found the actual pedalling action brought your feet close together. Within five minutes I realised that this was my idea.

What helps you go faster, the bike or the position?
It's everything together. If I didn't have the position there wouldn't be the same need

Aiming to put twenty years of cycling design to the test, Boardman starts by riding an old-style drop handle-barred machine — it will be a yardstick with which to compare later developments.

for the narrow bracket allowing knees closer together because, on a normal bicycle, it's not quite as important because you're not as bent over. It's when you get bent over that the knees tend to draw in together towards each other. I think if I'd a normal bike like Chris Boardman's bike then I would still be quick. But for my body, the way I'm built, maybe with long arms and the way I'm used to cycling, a low position might be my most natural position.

Boardman's own track cycle proves significantly faster than the 'racer' of a previous generation.

■ Boardman is more ready to acknowledge his debt to Windcheetah and technology as well as voicing fears over the threat the success of such bikes poses to the sport. If Obree is the innovator, his rival is the purist. In Boardman's ideal world, all bikes would be equal and the winner would be the best athlete. That this is not the case has converted him into a reluctant cycling scientist. Even a sporting Luddite wants to win. ▶

Q. What is your attitude to Graeme Obree's bike?
CHRIS BOARDMAN: Graeme Obree follows exactly the same philosophy as I do, because Graham doesn't accept the norms. In some ways it is a shame for both of us, because there's a lot of tradition in society. Graeme has said, "OK, I don't accept that this is the position for riding a bicycle", and went out and found a different way to do it.

That it was very successful has scared quite a few people in cycling, because somebody's pushed the rules further, but you've got to be open-minded to succeed nowadays, because if you rest on the same ideas that have always been, then you're going to come up with the same performances. To push the level of performance, you must always question.

Do you have to test his methods?
Although I don't like it, and I don't consider it to be cycling, if it is within the rules, then I must try it. I want to evaluate what is the best way to ride a bike, to go fastest for a given event within the rules. Hopefully my bike's just as good, but we don't know.

Has cycling become simply a battle of technology?
I think the problem that a lot of people in the cycling world face is that you will always have the very good athletes at the top, but somebody who's not the best might make the difference by coming up with a clever idea. In effect, you could have an inventor winning a bike race, and that'll be sad. I think the likes of Graham Obree would still be in the top four or five in the world, because he's a superb athlete. But being able to ride in such a radically different position may give him that edge.

■ It is perhaps a blessing that Boardman - or even, for that matter, the more open minded Obree - never took up javelin throwing. Cycling has undoubtedly been influenced by technological progress, but the speciality appears technically virginal

Last of all, the Obree look-a-like cycle proves fractionally faster — Boardman felt the body position enabled him to work harder against the pedals. But will he ride one? He hasn't yet decided.

compared with the harlot to innovation that the javelin has become.

Since the early 1980s, the javelin world record has been as likely to be affected by findings in the wind tunnels of Europe (and the committee rooms of the sport's governing bodies where equipment specifications and new records are ratified) as it has on the track where athletes participate in the ancient discipline. The bureaucratic effort to undermine consistently successful research into the aerodynamics of the javelin has been for the best reason. Improvements in design had began to endanger enthralled spectators at the far end of the stadium.

In 1984, the East German, Uwe Hohn broke the 100 metres barrier for the first time with a world record javelin throw of nearly 105 metres. In the smaller athletic stadiums scheduled to hold international events, Hohn's throw meant the safety of the crowd could only be guaranteed for a few more years if technological advances continued to enhance the athletes' ability to throw further. The authorities redrafted the specifications of the javelin, moving the centre of gravity further forward, so it would not fly as far. The world record slate was wiped clean accordingly.

Britain's Steve Backley set a fresh world best with the newly designed impaler. But the innovators would not be denied their triumph. Jan Zelezny, from the former Czechoslovakian republic achieved a new all time record with a javelin sporting a roughened tail. Its designer, Miklos Nemeth, himself a former world record holder and Olympic Champion, had taken the principle that compels golf ball manufacturers to dimple their product and applied it to the javelin. The result was a new mark. Once Backley adopted the new design, he recaptured the world record.

But when Seppo Raty, threw nearly 97 metres, spectators were, once again, in danger. Fearful of another break-through the authorities declared the "pimpled one" illegal and gave the record back to Backley, who did not need so much as to venture into the stadium to assume the title. Things returned to normal.

But Jan Zelezny was not finished. He returned with a javelin, which, on the face of it, seemed pretty ordinary; long and thin, weighing around 800 grammes, with a sharp end that stuck into the ground. Its special design revealed itself only in flight. When airborn, javelins usually wiggle. This one didn't and went further.

A carbon sheath kept the smooth flying projectile free from vibration. Seats at the far end of the stadium were, once again, going cheap. Zelezny comfortably regained the record he lost in 1988. Not surprisingly, the authorities found fault with his equipment. Backley's record was reinstated and the wiggle-free javelin outlawed (for having a fourth part - the sheath - in addition to the grip, shaft and point, the three constitute parts that are allowed). Zelezny, at least, had the final word. He threw a javelin of normal specifications over 95 metres to take the record once again.

For those who take a historical view of sport, the last decade's tomfoolery has all but destroyed the credibility of the concept "Javelin world record". Thanks to technology, its holder could, in some way, be less talented that his compromised rivals. More appropriate than the suffix "WRH", after an athlete's name, would be some sort of

recognition in the sports design community for advances in Javelin technology.

At least, with Boardman's criticism in mind, the basics of javelin as a competitive sport are still respected, the kudos of the world record apart. It remains a case of simply throwing it. The Olympic, European and Commonwealth ruling bodies catch up with technological advancements in the tool of the trade promptly. On-the-day, major championship competition is usually unaffected. There is not a great lag between innovation, official assessment and action. Few athletes experiment in the championship final. Consequently, medals are rarely won by untalented innovators.

Diving medals are also usually awarded on merit, save for the occasional judging

Steve Backley (right) among a field of javelins. As throwing technique has improved, javelin design has been altered to keep distances under control.

Having missed a European Championship Gold Medal by the smallest margin in the history of diving, Robert Morgan now uses every hi-tech means available with the intention of redressing the balance.

controversy. In this discipline, advantages from technology used in the actual competition are in short supply. Wales' Bobby Morgan is in the top six in the world at ten metre diving. In his discipline, it is just Morgan, the board, some space and the water that determine whether he impresses the judges.

Technological advances in diving have been restricted to the training pool. If the latest fad had been available in 1993, Morgan, Britain's best diver, would now be referred to as the European champion. In Sheffield that year he lost out to Dimitri Sautin by a margin of 0.03 points. It was the narrowest margin in the history of the sport. Months on he can be philosophical. He maintains it was his best performance in a major competition - he came fifth in Barcelona the year before - and strengthened his self belief.

At the time, Morgan also knew his enhanced confidence alone would not be enough to lift him up that one notch to gold. The winner, a determined Russian who will be back, enjoyed an even bigger moral booster: victory. After finishing so close, Morgan knew he had to find extra points, plus interest, to secure Olympic gold.

Morgan turned to the most sophisticated technology available to divers in pursuit of the illusive 0.03 plus points. As a golfer - "diving is like golf, it is the same game, its

Bio-mechanics expert John Newton analyses Robert Morgan's performance using high-speed film and digital computer imagery.

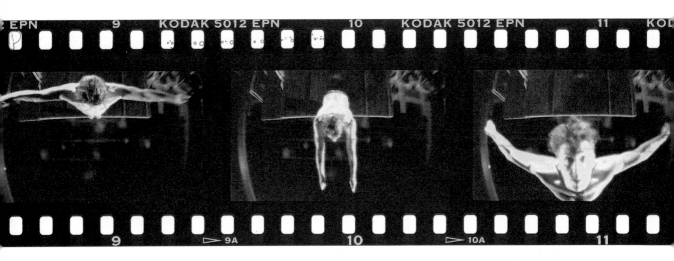

keeping yourself straight-minded" - Morgan accepts advances in his tools as serenely as he hits a dimpled golf ball, sure in the knowledge that the depressions will make it go further as did Miklos Nemeth's javelin.

Morgan took advantage of the modern methods available to analyse his performance so that the next time he found himself ten metres above the water in the European Championships, he would not fail to take gold by such an agonising margin. John Newton, his "second coach" is head of biomechanics at Leeds Metropolitan University. Together they went about analysing the Russian conqueror's dives and Morgan's weaknesses and strengths using high speed film. The film confirmed to Newton what his instincts suspected. Morgan's take off wasn't good enough – and once a diver is in the air, there is little he can do to improve the dive.

The revelations of the video presented a challenge. Morgan was 26, an age when the majority of divers - indeed most sportsmen - are pretty much set in their ways. Nevertheless, they persevered. The combination of solid proof on film, courtesy of some of the most sophisticated cameras money can buy, and Morgan's obvious determination to succeed, produced results. Months afterwards, Newton, a happy. bubbly character most of the time, had good reason to be cheerful. ▶

High-speed film analysis revealed Morgan's problem to be his take-off from the platform. This is the last moment a diver has real control over his body position.

Q. What work did you do with Bob Morgan using the video camera?

JOHN NEWTON: We started seriously working with Bob after the European championships in 1993 which we filmed for analysis purposes. We had some suspicions that there were weaknesses in Bobby's take-off technique. When we came to analyse the data from the European's we found one of his biggest faults was actually on the take-off for the three and a half front somersault. And, at the level we're working at, every little bit counts. We compared Bobby's take off with the winner, Dimitri Sautin and found some very interesting things occurring that you couldn't see from the pool side.

Unless take-off is perfect, a diver stands little chance of entering the water smoothly.

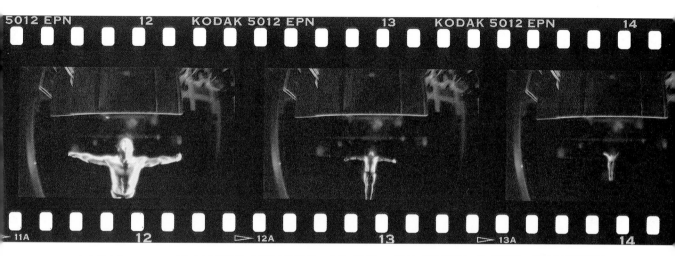

We found, in effect, that he was falling off the end of the board instead of pushing his body off the end of the board.

How did Bob's dive compare with the winner's?

Dimitri Sautin jumped into the dive. Watching the video, we saw how straight his body was and the position his arms were reaching up and down. He was pushing his hips up in the air with his trunk fairly upright. We saw how high he was above the board itself, probably about 30 or 40 centimetres above. When we looked at Bobby Morgan doing the same dive we found that Bob's arms never reached behind his head, they always caused him to lean forward. When he hit the end of the board, after his leap, his trunk just fell forward. When Bobby started, his legs were horizontal through the first somersault and he was only level with the board, so he was a good 20 to 30 centimetres below the winner on his take off position. It had a tremendous effect on the way down because the judges get the impression of how high you are when you come out of your dive and already, before he'd even passed the board, Bobby was losing. When we analysed it, Bobby's actual centre of gravity did not go up, it fell off the end of the board and that was very significant.

Could you change the dive?

We tried to get Bobby to push more when his centre of gravity was over his feet. We had to stop him leaning his trunk forward on contact with the end of the board. We had to change his arm action slightly and get his chest up. And we had some success. It's hard to change but it worked. Nobody attempted to change it for him, but we think we made a significant difference.

■ Newton and technology gave Bobby Morgan more time in the air. It looks like the combination has saved his career from stagnation, albeit at a high level. In 1988, Morgan's career was also under threat during what he describes as a "funky" year. This was repeated in 1990. During these two 12 month spells of competition, he "lost" his dives. A lot of diving is creating a strong positive image in your mind about the demands ahead. In 1988 and again two years later, Morgan could not even visualise doing a forward somersault off a one metre board.

Now, master of his own diving mind again and having benefited from the most recent developments available to divers, Morgan is back on course to win medals. Advances in equipment have helped many other athletes. Even Boardman, less inclined than most to embrace progress unless it is proven to him, gives some of the credit for his gold medal to the efforts of the Lotus design team. He did, after all, speculate after Barcelona that, without the bike, he might have managed only bronze.

In gymnastics, modifications in equipment have been less welcomed by some competitors. Women's gymnastics is a young person's sport. This has not always been the case, but it is increasingly felt that 20 years and over is a pensionable age. Many of

Aware for the first time of his dives' deficiencies, Morgan is seeing definite improvements in his performance. 'An Olympic medal starts here,' he says.

WOMEN'S GYMNASTICS - OR GIRL'S GYMNASTICS ?

Gymnastics for girls and women is now more popular than baseball in the United States, according to a television popularity poll. It was the most watched event in the 1992 Barcelona Olympics.

At the highest level, gymnasts have shrunk. Around 30 years ago Olympic gymnasts were an average 25 pounds heavier and four inches taller than they are today.

The more competition, the more complicated the routines have become. Nadia Comaneci, the famous Romanian gymnast, was the first to score a perfect ten in an Olympic competition, yet today her routines would only score 9.2.

The smaller you are the more space you have to do complex routines. There is a logic to the advantage size can give you on the different apparatus - the beam, the floor, the asymmetric bars, and the vault.

Think of the advantage you get if your foot fits on the beam. Olympic teams are now made up of girls - not women - because of the height and weight advantage they have by competing so young.

Some senior figures in gymnastics are concerned about the pressure advice to `keep your weight low` can have on such an impressionable age group. Puberty inevitably brings weight changes that some young gymnasts try to resist - with subsequent risks of bad nutrition or eating disorders.

"We should enlarge the dimensions of the equipment: increasing the floor area, the width and length of the beam, the gap between the uneven bars - all of this would contribute to allow larger, more adult-sized women to be more successful. If everyone can use the equipment in the same way, then we have a level playing field"

Don Peters, ex-US Olympic coach

Britain's top female performers are struggling with exams at school as well as facing up to the challenge of the vault. As a result of changes in equipment, this is an accelerating trend. Gymnasts are expected to perform moves of gymnastic maturity before they have evolved from children into early womanhood. Post-pubescent women gymnasts are now a rarity with few continuing to perform beyond their late teens.

Vince Walduck is a professional gymnastics coach as well as an ex-national gymnast. He trains Zita Lusack (above), one of Britain's most gifted natural performers in many of the respective disciplines. Most in Walduck's care are teenagers. ▶

Q. Why do 20-year-olds and older no longer do well in women's gymnastics?
VINCE WALDUCK: The sport has moved on, the apparatus has changed, the level of difficulty has just escalated to an incredible level. You have to be super-skilled with a super human body to be able to do world class gymnastics and it's only a young person in the ten to 16 category that can compete and perform some of the complex elements.

How have changes in the equipment affected the sport?
Over the last 20 years, the apparatus has changed quite considerably. The floor is much springier, and therefore allows the gymnast to jump a little higher. It also helps in preventing injury because when you contact the floor with such force, the feet and ankles are much more prone to stress injuries. The bar rails have changed and become fibreglass, and the distance between the bars has increased. The vaulting horse is now sprung. The women's bars are smaller which mirrors the change in women's gymnastics bar work, which has tended to mirror a lot of the men's high bar movements. Small children have small hands so holding onto a smaller bar is easier, and the more pliable it is, the more springy it helps them to do the more complex circling and somersault movements.

■ Youth already had many advantages over experience in a sport like gymnastics before changes to the equipment accentuated the importance of size and weight. Generally, nature is already on the side of the young athlete in sport without the tools of the trade making it even harder for more developed competitors to make an impression. Gymnastics is even less forgiving towards "veterans" over 20 than other disciplines. ▶

Q. Is gymnastics a young person's sport?
VINCE WALDUCK: You can study when you're 60, you can do an Open University degree, you can go back and do school exams whatever age you are, but you can't be a

'If you have a lady's proportions then you can't do the difficult elements in gymnastics. It's impossible.'

THE MAIN CONTENDERS

CHRIS BOARDMAN
Date of Birth: 26 August 1968
Height: 5' 9" / 1.75 m
Weight: 11st 5lbs / 72 kg

COMPETITION RECORD:
4000m Pursuit Cycling: He set a world one hour record with a distance of 52,270 km at Bordeaux on 23 July, 1993.
He signed professional terms with the French team GAN shortly afterwards.

1992 Olympic champion. He set a pre-Games best of 4:31.4, set Olympic records of 4:27.357 and 4:24.496 - the latter was recognised as a world record.

Boardman won Commonwealth bronze at team pursuit in 1988 and has also won a series of national titles.

Zita Lusack is one of Britain's most talented natural gymnasts, but is nearing the end of her career at the age of sixteen.

gymnast once you've turned 18 really. The aim in gymnastics is to work before the young girl turns into a young lady because then the body weight changes, the body proportions are less.

What exactly are the advantages?
If you're smaller, you can rotate and twist faster in a given air space. On the bars it helps in that you can accelerate your body quicker because you have to change shape less to miss the low bar. On tumbling, when you're allowed to run into your somersault runs, a smaller gymnast can get in more strides and generate more speed than a taller girl, who might be able to manage perhaps only four strides. It is the same on beam. The smaller girl can fit in more complex somersaults and difficult skills in a linked line. If you are too heavy then you cannot perform at your best, if you are carrying around additional fat it's like carrying around a bag of potatoes on each hip, it puts more strain on your body and you're more likely to become injured.

Why is youth so important?
Before she has developed, a young girl is much more able to learn difficult skills than after puberty. They're much faster.

Does that mean, if you're a woman, you haven't got much hope?
If you have a lady's proportions then you can't do the difficult elements in gymnastics. It's impossible. Gravity moves and that's the scientific part of it. The crucial thing is your height/body weight ratio. Gymnastics is a sport where you are dealing with your own body weight. It's not like a shot putter who is dealing with an object where

The Quest for the Perfect Athlete

What are the absolute limits of athletic performance? The fastest man? The highest pole vaulter? The furthest javelin throw? The short answer is that no one knows, and people who have guessed in the past have usually got it wrong. It wasn't that long ago that people were claiming that the four minute mile was an impossible barrier to beat. Now it is done almost routinely.

Records keep falling. Most recently, as greater numbers of women enter the sporting arena, their records have been broken at an even quicker rate than their male counterparts.

"It's not any one thing, it's a combination of factors. Different tracks, world-wide competition, better application of science, but most importantly a much larger pool of people from which to draw on. A hundred years ago the world's best sprinter might have spent his life working in a hat factory."

Dr. Ralph Mann, Compusport, USA.

Dr. Ralph Mann, an ex-Olympic hurdler and a biomechanist who works in conjunction with the American Olympic team, has investigated the theoretical limits of athletes. By understanding the physical constraints of running he can create a computer animation of a perfect sprinter or hurdler. The ingenious next step is to then use this perfect athlete to boost the performance of real athletes. Quincy Watts, the former 400m Olympic gold medallist, has been one of his guinea pigs.

The precise body measurements of Watts were fed into the computer. This enabled a perfect animated model of Watts to be made. This was then compared with the real thing, filmed in slow motion at a competition. Any discrepancies between the "ideal" Watts and the "real" one were easily spotted. In this case, it involved him sitting a fractionally further back than his computer model. By adjusting his stride it would be possible to shave off vital time from each of his strides.

"We're not talking about much, fractions of a millisecond. But if you add up all the time saved for each stride, and you're saving a tenth of a millisecond per stride it soon begins to add up, possibly making the difference between a gold and an also-ran."

Many US athletes have benefited from Ralph Mann's work: Butch Reynolds and Michael Johnson among others. It is by the application of sophisticated technology that modern athletes can get an edge on their rivals and in doing so, push back the frontiers of human performance.

increased muscle strength and bulk can propel the thing further. Gymnastics is a child's sport. To be world class you have to have a very light body weight. It has developed so that usually only pre-pubescent children, under 17, can compete.

Is that a good or a bad thing?
One can argue that it is a shame that the field is so narrow, that you can only be a top gymnast between the ages of 13 and 17, but it's been determined by the complexity of the sport. If Britain wants to try and keep up with the rest of the world she has to follow that.

What is it that 13 to 17 year-olds can do that ordinary people can't ? What gives them an advantage?
The average body fat of a lady is around 22 per cent of her total weight. The body fat of a child is usually lower and the muscular strength, in comparison to their light frame, puts them at quite an advantage.

When do you feel that gymnasts should retire?
As they change and grow up they become heavier. If you start to put on weight and become, in what we would call in gymnastics terms, fat (which could be normal for a

teenager) it puts more strain on the joints. It becomes impossible to do difficult elements. Because the sport is so demanding at the top level, the body and the joints can only take so much wear and tear. It's not a sport that you can go on doing into your 20s, at a high level. There is also psychological burn out. At top level it requires 30 hours a week training and the strain and monotony of coming to the gym, day in, day out, for that sort of intensity of training, is difficult to cope with for too long.

■ The dilemma from a coaching point of view is that more mature athletes would undoubtedly cope better with the related hardships of the training. Lusack is a young athlete with an even younger temperament. In this respect she is not much different to most teenage girls of her background. Teen years can be a difficult time. Her coach, Walduck's difficulty is that the clock is already running out for her protégé. As she grows older, the likelihood of her fulfilling her potential in the sport receedes.

Lusack has no real self-confidence in her abilities as a gymnast. While she enjoys being at the gym - it brings companionship and rapport with other girls of a similar age - it seems that the sport that requires her to be there holds little appeal in its own right. She hates competition, and has trouble sleeping and eating beforehand. In the gym she rarely looks cheerful. Her relationship with her coach is not great, although his expertise is undoubtedly of value to her, even if he struggles to motivate a very unmotivated young lady.

To blame all this on the tools of the trade - the changes in equipment - would overlook the personalities involved. It may just be that the Lusack/Walduck team is not fated to fulfil its every dream. Nevertheless, a sport that has no room for those above 20 years of age and that makes demands on competitors like Zita Lusack long before she is mature enough to cope adequately, may have lost the element of fun that ensures there is a steady stream of willing players to replace the current generations.

If it is lucky Chris Boardman does not throw the javelin, it is even more fortunate that he does not have to put up with the technology in female gymnastics.

SHOES

Athletic footwear has always been the source of controversy. Do special shoes really improve the athlete's performance or is it just hype? The shoe makers bank on the fact that young people will try and copy their idols and buy the shoes they see their heroes wear on television. However, Martin Steele argues that there are only three things that you need to know about running shoes; they are all pretty much the same, the fancy add-ons don't make much of a difference, and they are all over-priced.

Weightlifting

The sole of a weightlifter's shoes are made of wood. Before they make a lift they coat the sole of the shoe with resin. This is to give them better grip when they are on the stage.

Shooters

Shooters have shoes with as large an area of sole as they are allowed. This means that the soles of shoes stick out way beyond the uppers of the shoe proper. The rules permit only so much sole.

Long distance runners.

The "buzz word" here is orthotics. They are the plastic in-soles with orthopaedic properties. Many long distance runners swear that they have been an enormous benefit to their health while running, minimising the damage of the many foot strikes during racing.

Bare feet

Some runners don't bother with shoes at all. Zola Budd was famous for running barefoot. Also, many Kenyans run barefoot. It doesn't seem to do their performances much harm.

BANNED KIT

For every new piece of equipment that appears in the sporting arena, there's an army of sporting officials checking on its legality. Usually there are sensible reasons for banning a new piece of equipment, such as the javelins which were so aerodynamic they were a hazard to spectators in the stadium, but there will always be sports equipment manufacturers and athletes who try and bend the rules to their advantage.

SPEEDO AUSTRALIA LYCRA/NEOPRENE SUIT

For the Seoul Olympics, 1988, Speedo Australia developed a new Lycra/neoprene suit that they claimed carved seconds off times. They claimed it worked because the water flowed around the suits rather than through them. Unfortunately the neoprene also added extra buoyancy and the Olympic authorities banned them because they constituted a 'flotation device'.

TOKYO RUNNING TRACK

It's unusual to think of a running track as a piece of kit but, as far as the runners are concerned, it's as important as the shoes they have on their feet. The Tokyo running track was a state-of-the-art track for the 1991 World Championships. Unfortunately it was too good. The bounce generated by the track's surface was literally spurring the runners on. Times were shattered and the sporting authorities stepped in. No longer can times from that track count as proper records.

OBREE'S BIKE

In 1993, Graham Obree developed a revolutionary bike out of spare washing-machine parts. It worked, but it has been banned by cycling's world governing body because it is too unstable to be safe.

FILMING BOB MORGAN

Watching Bob Morgan and his training partners at Sheffield's fantastic Ponds Forge pool dive, one is struck by two things. The first is that it looks beautiful, and the second is that they must be mad. From the ten metre platform a diver hits the water at over 30 miles per hour. It is fast enough to kill if the entry is not pulled off perfectly: Bob himself has twice been dragged unconscious from the pool because of a misjudgement in the one and a half seconds a dive takes from leap to water surface. In filming him we wanted to emphasise this tension in the sport: grace in the face of danger. We wanted also to capture the divers in both the elements they work in: air and water. In the air they are like astronauts on a space-walk - their long, slow, open dives have a weightless quality and they seem to float from the platform. We decided to capture this by taking a leaf from the NASA book of film images. Everyone must have seen at some time the glorious wide angle images of the earth taken from Apollo spacecraft or the Space Shuttle: the blue surface curves towards the lens in the centre and slips away at each side, the space-walking astronaut distorting as they come towards the camera. We wanted to create this same effect for the divers, so we suspended a film camera with a very wide angle lens directly over their heads, twelve metres above the surface of the water. Where NASA photographed the earth curving away in the background, we would have the blue of the diving pool, made round by the curvature of the lens, and our astronaut would be the diver rising towards the lens, hanging in mid air and then falling backwards for what seems like miles, into the water.

The contrast to the outwardly glamorous show of the dive is what happens underwater. Whereas the dive through the air is free and fast, the water is constricting and silent and slow - where the one is flamboyant and theatrical, the other is private and subdued. For the crowd, the dive finishes at the water surface and there is merely a brief interlude before the performer reappears. Yet for the diver, underwater is when they know how they have performed and they have a few seconds alone before they surface to the eyes of the judges and the world. In many ways, underwater is where they are most at home. We wanted to feel close to them in this environment too, to share with them the moments when, as Bob said to us, "you feel you've just cut the water surface, you drill downwards and you know people are saying 'Wow!' and you rise back to the surface and you're going to come up

In these pictures, and those on pages 94 and 95, we hope we have captured some of the grace and excitement of diving. Filming Robert Morgan was one of the most enjoyable moments in the series.

and say 'Wait there! I've got some more coming like that!'."

We decided that the only way to share these few seconds was to put a diver of our own into the water with an underwater camera. Rob Franklin, our underwater photographer, was able to get within a few feet of the exploding water surface as the divers smashed their way in, their hands not pointed to break the water's tension but flat to punch a hole for their body. He was able to swim around them as they powered to the pool floor twenty feet down, and he could share with them the elation of the gentle rise to the surface, the bubbles of their dramatic entry against their skin.

Filming Bobby was one of the most enjoyable and rewarding experiences of the series. We hope we have done him justice. R.D.

MIND GAMES

"The pressure is enormous: this is not just my job, it is all I am, all I shall ever be... for all time."

Graeme Obree, World pursuit cycling champion

thletics rarely endures the full modern-day tabloid treatment the modern British press is capable of. Since newspapers went "splash happy", the great successes of track and field have been ably chronicled - Wells, Coe, Ovett, and Cram, from the past, Christie, Gunnell, Jackson, among others from today's stars - but other sports have stolen the more outrageous spreads.

The unfortunate experiences of Matthew Yates was, however, too bizarre a story for even the most considerate new editor to let pass unrecorded.

It has not affected Yates unduly in the long-run. A year after his experiences at the Barcelona Olympics which drew the attention of the Fourth Estate, he was ranked Britain's number one 1500 metre runner. Not bad for an athlete who, 12 months earlier inspired the headline in one of Britain's more popular newspapers: "Oh Dear What Can the Matter Be, Matthew Yates is Stuck in the Lavatory".

Another unforgivable, if humorous tabloid excess? It is an old tune. It was, however, and some might say unusually for journals of this nature, a true story. Well, at least partly true. The suggestion was that Yates, desperate not to run in his 1500 metres Olympic heat had sought sanctuary in the men's room. The reality only half confirmed the Daily Star's tuneful jibe. Yates did, indeed, go to the toilet, moments before running, but the visit was a routine matter, "something sportsmen just do, you feel comfortable". The true part of the conjecture was that Yates really felt no inclination to compete. It was the biggest race of his life, but he decided, quite coldly and clinically not to line up and compete for a place in the Olympic final of the 1500 metres, the Blue Riband event of the games.

The Daily Star missed the real story. The competition should have been the culmination of a career of hard training, but Yates decided not run. Why? Yates' preparation, leading up to the games had gone well. A few weeks before the contest, he

Graeme Obree. Twenty-eight-year-old failed bike-shop owner from Irvine, and World Pursuit Cycling Champion.

believed he was in good shape and commentators busied themselves, instead of mischieving, with talk of medals. Not to run seemed madness. The Daily Star's concern was not misplaced. What, indeed, was the matter with Matt Yates?

Physically, it seemed there was little wrong with Britain's outstanding middle distance medal hope of the games. His training suggested all was well. He had recorded some sparkling times in workouts. The clock had heightened the media's interest in his prospects for the forthcoming Olympics. There was little to indicate, on the surface, what was to follow. In fact, Matt Yates was pretty sick with plasmic pneumonia (pneumonia in the blood). This malaise does not usually manifest itself in tangible side-effects (if you exclude the sight of a gifted athlete under-performing). It struck into his subconscious with an evil vengence and, very soon, there was hardly any of the self-belief that his times and work outs warranted. The pressure athletes are under today, accentuated by the attentions of the tabloids, is much greater than in any time in the sport's history. Athletics has always been the provost of the individual. The British Olympic team is not like Manchester United. The former is the sum of parts, the latter a whole. Mentally, Matt Yates, low with a blood disorder, was simply not equipped to deal with, borrowing the inspiration of the novel, the loneliness of a long distance runner. If he wasn't hiding in the toilet, he certainly felt like locking himself away somewhere other than Barcelona. ▶

Q. How would you describe your situation before the race in terms of your mental and physical state?

MATTHEW YATES: Physically things were going awfully well and the training was working fine. I was doing some awesome times on the track. But to me it wasn't equating with the way I felt. I was very low and I doubted what I could do. I had zero confidence about what would happen at the Olympics. Most gold medalists from the games would have been on par with my training, but where they would have got me was their mental ability in the games, which I had not got. It was non-existent.

How did you know that you were in such good physical form?
The clock told me I was in good form. The clock was there with the times, telling me I was running fast and I was running good in training. But it was no good. I probably could have run a personal best and I still would have been mentally down. The clock would've been wrong or there would've been something wrong with the time. That's the way training was before. People just couldn't believe the sessions I was running. But for me, I almost got to the point where I thought my coach was telling me the wrong times to make me feel better.

How would you sum up your situation mentally and physically at that time?
Physically I was fine. Mentally , below zero. I mean it's basically as if the physical side was saying "yes I'm ready", and the mental side was saying "no", and the mental side

really does control most of you as an athlete - especially prior to something as big as the Olympics. It told me physically I wasn't capable of doing it. The physical side agreed with the mental side in the end.

What hype was there about you before the Olympics?
Beforehand, I was a predicted medal hope for the Olympics in the 1500 metres. I was coming of age. I was living in the shadow of Coe, Ovett, and Cram and I was to be the next one.

Why was the pressure so intense on you during the Olympics?
Not having been to an Olympics before, I didn't really know how big it was. It is massive. Barcelona is a big place and it stopped for that games. When you look back on it, *the world* had really stopped for the games. There, you realise that you're one of the reasons why the world is stopping. You're a competitor at the Olympics. You're a sports person come to compete in the world games. It's pretty awesome. It suddenly hits you. People are paying to sit in seats and watch. As soon as you arrive at the Olympic Village,

Matthew Yates. In top physical form at the Barcelona Olympics, he should have taken a 1500 metre medal. He never even made the final.

111

and there are people waiting for autographs outside, you realise what it's about and it's pretty scary.

How is the pressure on you compared to a footballer?
If I was to play football I could have a bad game and ten guys could have a good game and we could still win, but when I'm running round the track I can make one bad move, not be able to recover, and people see the result as I'm coming down the home straight in third or fourth or whatever and not winning. It's there for everyone to see. The first across the line is obviously the best on the day. The Olympics is there to prove that. It's about being the best on that chosen day. And everyone knows when the chosen day is. Everyone's got to get ready for that day.

■ The Olympic Games is the biggest sporting event in the world. If an athlete or performer is under pressure then the Olympics is the one sure-fire occasion that will make them crack. A fit and well Matt Yates was talented and capable enough to deal with it. The Matthew Yates in Barcelona, his mental resolve weakened, was not.

It didn't help that he also saw a graveyard. Athletes are notoriously superstitious. Yates is no different. Some won't run on cracks in the pavement, others go through strange methodical rituals of preparation. Yates' thing is graveyards. The sight of one in Barcelona before running was a crushing blow. If it had been a magpie it would have been fine, he could have saluted it. But not a graveyard. For Matt Yates, seeing a graveyard on a bend in the road means failure is waiting just around the corner. Strange maybe, but about par for the course in the deeply neurotic world of track and field. In this respect, perfectly understandable!

The burden of expectation, perceived or otherwise, also weighed heavy on an already overloaded mind. A sports shoe manufacturer had made shoes especially for the heir to a modern middle-distance track legacy passed first from Brendan Foster to Coe and Ovett and then on to Steve Cram and Peter Elliott. There was the Yates family and assorted relatives, too, not forgetting a world-wide television audience.

All Yates wanted to avoid was letting all these people down. The best way to head off disappointment, Yates concluded, was not to run. In fact, he did. He describes qualifying from his heat for the semi-finals as, in the circumstances, the best run of his life. Then came defeat in the semi-finals. He was soundly beaten. Shortly afterwards, he left Spain, if not humiliated, then certainly humbled. ▶

Q. How did the pressure make you feel before the competition?
MATTHEW YATES: I was very scared to fail, which was one of the problems. It was a world stage, At home, people were watching. People were going to be reading about it the next day as well. And I didn't want to fail . No-one wants to fail in any walk of life, and if they do they've got a problem. And I didn't want to fail. It wasn't a driving force within me to push me on. It was holding me back. Looking back at it now, I realise that I should

have just gone with the flow , and relaxed more.

How did you feel as you were coming up to the start of your heat in the Olympics?
Highly emotional, the hairs on my back were up and there was water in my eyes. No sooner are you out on the track than they're telling you to take your kit off, and get ready to race. I turned round and got my lanes wrong. I looked up and the flame was up there flickering away, and it's the Olympic Games. It suddenly hit me. It was almost as if it was in slow motion. We stood there silently and the crowd noise level dropped. Next the television cued in the race and I was called to the marks, and bang we were off. I think after 100 metres I took the lead. And I didn't get overtaken till about 180 metres to go. I didn't even have time to gather my thoughts walking across the track. You are ushered off the track very quickly. I was very relieved. I had done a deal with myself that, even if I did qualify from the round, I would still review running in the semi finals.

But you did run again?
I ran and, you know the end result. I finished last. I was quite happy that I was going home. I was signed out the of the games. It was almost as if I was being signed out of war. You are happy, you are going home from war because it's over for you. That was the case for me and a lot of pressure lifted. As soon as I could I got out of Barcelona and went back to London.

When you were still in Barcelona did you ever feel lonely?
I did feel lonely in the Olympic Village. I had friends out there , but I don't think they really understood what the problems were. They were trying their best , but I don't thing they really comprehended them as such. I did feel very alone.

What happened when you saw the graveyard?
As the bus was going along the motorway, I looked up and the graveyard was there. For me to see a graveyard was extremely bad news. Graveyards mean failure to me. It's not an association with death or anything like that, it's just that I'd seen graveyards before in competitions where I'd run badly. The automatic negative thoughts didn't creep into my mind, they stormed into my mind, and they said: you're going fail. Once that was in my head, that was it.

Revisiting the scene of what he calls his 'biggest failure', Yates feels he has learnt some important lessons.

What did you see when you looked at your special shoes. What did you feel?
I remember sitting underneath the stand and putting on these specially made shoes for myself - with my name on the back - and suddenly thinking "these ain't gonna work". You know, what have they done this for? I'm going to fail. Everything had come together and I was going to fail. I *told* myself before I was going to fail, and that the shoes weren't going to make any difference to me. "Ain't going to bring my any luck."

Did you feel lonely on the track?
Basically, when you walk out into this stadium with 80,000 people, (and what seems like the noise of 200,000) it's very much like being an animal in a cage. You're in there, you can't do anything about it and you're on your own. And everyone's making a noise and looking at you. They've come to look at you. It must be like that for an animal in a cage. They can't do anything about it. They're just wandering round. I felt very lonely and the crowd's time was different to my time. They were going faster than I was out on the track. Everything that I was seeing, I was taking in; smells, noise, sights. It was so new that I could've been in the middle of Alaska or something.

Was everything in slow motion?
It *is* like when you have a car accident, everything just goes slow. And it was like one of those Westerns where people die slowly, and that's how I was going.

■ It is a graphic tale that says more about athletics than it does about Yates. He was largely left to suffer alone by indifferent officials who saw him as "a waste of time". Today the sport has become psychological warfare as well as the pursuit of physical excellence. Debates rage about whether the athletes of the 1990s are more naturally gifted than the first Olympians, or if modern conditions, technology, and other advances account for the improvements in times achieved, distances thrown, and points awarded. What few dispute, is that greater mental resolve is required to compete in major championships today. With respect to past champions, the Olympic and Commonwealth Games, the World and European Championships of the 1990s, are not for the faint hearted. In years gone by, the traumas of Matt Yates would probably never have happened.

On first sight, Shirley McIntosh would not seem the most likely candidate for this challenge of international competition in the stress-filled sports arenas of the 1990s. Training for her discipline - three position shooting - is fitted around auditing and motherhood. That she shoulders the additional burden of a family and a career away from sport is reason to pay even greater homage to the Scot for breaking the British women's record for three position shooting, as well as annexing the National championships in 1993.

Shooting is unusual in the context of the overall Olympics in that the adrenaline rush that many athletes use and need to reach new record breaking heights in competition is

a disadvantage. The key word is control. Physically, the shooter has to be in complete command of every limb and every internal organ, particularly the heart and pulse. Even in the most nerve-wracking moments of international competition, the best shooters have developed the ability to reduce their heart beat. Physical fitness is more than important. The control that is so crucial to success in shooting - the slightest movement and the target is missed completely - is significantly more achievable if the competitor is in good shape. ▶

Q. Why is it important to be in good shape?
SHIRLEY McINTOSH: It's important to be able to be aware of what your body's doing during shooting. The heart rate increases as you pick up the rifle and as you put it down again, and all through the loading process. Part of the preparation for each shot involves actually bringing your heart rate back down to its normal level, so that you're actually in a fit state to shoot, to fire the particular shot that you're working on.

In many ways the ultimate mental challenge, shooters must maintain complete mental calm. Shirley McIntosh can actually reduce heart-rate through concentration — even at the climax of international competition.

Why is one's heart rate so important?
If your heart is going very, very quickly, then you end up having a pulse coming through the rifle and it's just shaking all the time. This makes it difficult to shoot.

What do you do to counteract this?
Sometimes pulses can be caused by your equipment, the way your position is set up. For example, if you have the sling to hold the gun in the wrong place on your arm, it can sometimes catch a blood vessel, which will cause pulsing, so you can adjust your position to your sling or whatever to get round that problem.

What happens during the actual shot?
You pick up the rifle and settle into a position. This will all be done without taking aim at the target. You'll concentrate on getting your breathing back to normal after lifting the rifle up, and getting the heart rate back to a more normal level. Then you look down the sights, and actually bring the target into aim. Then you settle down again, breathing carefully, and taking shallower breaths until the point when the shot is actually there, and is not moving. Then you fire the shot.

Do you hold your breath?
No. You don't hold your breath while you're firing. For a standing shot, you have to have a little bit of breath in your lungs. You can't go down to the lower residual level, because otherwise you just fall over, you'd be too relaxed. But you still have to be fairly relaxed, without breathing all the way out

■ There are few artificial aids to help McIntosh in her efforts to achieve "control". Music is a rare and useful tool. She uses it in a slightly more sophisticated way than simply playing Tina Turner records on entering the shooting range. Nevertheless, the principle is the same. Calm balads can mellow the mind when she feels over anxious, or conversely, loud, fast paced songs can rev up the adrenalin should she feel too low-key.

If you consider that shooting is one of the most mentally taxing Olympic disciplines, the overall conclusion is that marksmen, and women, are quite exceptional athletes. They are in complete control physically, as well as being mentally tough. There is no opportunity in a stressed situation for the shout or a scream of anguish - a release - that is permitted, certainly in track and field, in other events under the Olympic umbrella. The shooter must try and get psyched "down", not "up" in the hours and days before competition. To achieve this, going as it does against human nature, shooters have to be mentally rock solid. ▶

A well trained shooter can visualise the target in their mind's eye. Part of training is to try and hit the target with your eyes shut.

Q. What mental preparation do you do?
SHIRLEY McINTOSH: A lot about shooting is very, very much in the mind, and the training is aimed at trying to be able to reproduce a shot, time after time; a perfect shot every time that you pick up a gun. It involves a lot of mental rehearsal, knowing what the shot "looks like" and being able to imagine that in your mind. In the actual process of firing a shot, everything you do will be the same every time; at least that's the ideal. There are certain key words that we sometimes use to put ourselves into the right state

of mind. I think of a key word, something like, "holding", "steady", "calm", or "smooth", all very long words that you can draw out when you say them to yourself. Everything is sort of winding down, becoming more still and calm, as you fire the shot.

Do you use any gimmicks to prepare mentally?
I like to listen to music a lot. I have lots of different kinds of music I listen to. If I'm not feeling geared up enough for a match I listen to some faster music to get me back on track, or if I'm feeling a bit nervous about something I'll listen to more ballad type music, or something a bit slower and more mellow, to get me down into a better state of mind for a shooting competition.

How hard do you concentrate?
When you're shooting in a competition, or even in training, you have to try and not be aware of any other sounds going on around you, that you could be easily distracted by, particularly people moving about behind you, for example, or on the firing point next to you.

Do you achieve this by going into a meditational state of mind?
You have to concentrate so hard on the job in hand that you become absorbed by what you're doing. Your state of mind is such that you're in your mental process of actually firing the shot and nothing can distract you from it. You can go into auto pilot, where everything is just happening and you aren't aware of anything else that's going on

around you. You just become absorbed by it.

What happens to your body when you're in this state, in terms of your pulse and in terms of your breathing?
When you become very absorbed mentally in what you're doing, it has quite a calming influence on your body. It's one way of bringing your heart rate down to a normal level. If you breathe gently, not gasping or anything like that, it all helps you to become more absorbed in yourself.

Does your heart rate ever go below normal when you shoot?
Your heart rate is increased quite drastically by actually lifting up the 4.8 Kg rifle, and settling on aim, loading, and aiming. It all increases your heart rate quite a lot. You have to bring it back to normal.

Do some people achieve good results in training and then blow out in competition?
Shooting is quite a mental sport. There are lots of people who can shoot very, very well in training, but, when it comes to actual competition, they can't produce the goods, because they don't have the mental capacity, or the mental ability to cope with the pressures of competition.

Why is this?
These people may feel extra pressure shooting in competition. It may lead to tension in

their body, which they're not aware of - and they cannot do anything to control it - or increased pulse, increased breathing rate. This will affect their shooting. If they become particularly nervous they may not actually notice them, and that will cause problems when shooting.

How do you actually put your bullet through a 10.4 millimetre dot when you're standing 50 metres away from it?

You have to have everything right at the time; the shot appears and you just take it. You don't actually consciously hold it on, you should just sit there and you fire it, and it should go in the middle. When the gun is totally still, you feel you can't miss it and that you'll hit it every time.

■ The trance state is one frequently encountered on the track. Yvonne Murray talks vividly about the occasion when she passed Zola Budd, something of a heroine of hers, at Crystal Palace. She recalls that "everything seemed so quiet" even though Tommy Boyle, her coach told her the place had just gone bananas as she'd broken the 2000 metres world record. Shirley McIntosh, a fellow Scot, has to establish these "white moments" as they have been coined, every time she steps up to plug the target.

Take the atmosphere and occasion down a level or two and "white moments" suddenly become considerably more elusive. Imagine Yvonne Murray running on a wet Wednesday afternoon in a quarter-full East European stadium in qualifying heats that, even for major championships, are rarely sell outs. Harder in these circumstances to create a trance. Shooting demands that competitors almost remove themselves from such dull environments to achieve the appropriate state of mind.

Steve Backley faces a more complex problem than simply contriving regular "white moments". He has to be able to achieve control during the act of throwing his javelin so that his technique can be relied upon. As well, he has to summon up the determination and enthusiasm for the throw that will produce the adrenaline to ease the projectile into the 90 metre zone. McIntosh makes the taking of her shot seem like the most natural thing in the world. Backley has to provoke his own natural outburst to enhance his power when throwing, but still keep a handle on his technique. A poorly thrown javelin, no matter how forceful it has been propelled into the sky, will not travel distances to trouble the judges. Equally, a technically perfect effort will fall some way short of the required yardage if the competitive passion is missing.

Solving this physical and mental conundrum - "competitive control" - requires Backley to begin preparing psychologically for his event well before the day of competition. The focusing of his mind on the challenge of holding together his technique and also generating aggression sufficient to throw competitively isn't an after-thought. In reality, it begins days before the event with "visualisation". This enables Backley to complete a picture in his own mind of the combination of poise and passion that he needs to carry the javelin beyond the 90 metre mark and him to a gold medal.

Q. How do you focus yourself for competitions, as opposed to training?

STEVE BACKLEY: In competition, the adrenaline's obviously naturally flowing. I tune in more, I'm more concentrated, I've got blinkers on. The day before, someone might say something to me and I just won't hear it because I'm somewhere else, I'm almost at the stadium already preparing to throw. It's a lot easier to visualise because you're more focused. The picture's less likely to break up. You're very very focused on what the actual job in hand is.

When does the mental preparation begin?
If I was throwing tomorrow I'd already be thinking about it the day before. If I was competing in a week I'd be beginning to focus. It goes in waves, but certainly a day, two days before you compete you do a lot of throws in this visualisation state, getting ready for the big one.

What do you actually do when you're visualising?
You basically lie down in a symmetrical position so you are relaxed, and make yourself nice and comfortable, usually in a quiet room with some very quiet music. There are breathing techniques using the stomach which slows your metabolism down, slows your thinking down, and blocks out everything that's going on around you, so that you are the only thing that exists. And then you go round your body and relax each part, making it hot, cold, fast, slow. Then you move in your mind to somewhere familiar, that's very easy to see in the mind's eye - the gymnasium or the garden, wherever feels comfortable at the time - and start doing some stretching, the same as you might do to prepare for throwing. You might "go" for a jog and actually listen out to see who's about. Then you can jump all of a sudden to the track. You pick the javelin up in your mind and *feel* it and check everything on it, and start stabbing a short throw up and down the field. In warm-up in your head you can smell the grass and you can feel the sun, where the wind's blowing from, whoever you're training with, what you're wearing, everything, every tiniest detail will actually help you. Eventually, you come closer and closer to the actual throw. You take your kit off, you get down to your vest and shorts and you're still on the run up and then all of a sudden you can put yourself in the Olympics with 80,000 people there and you can hear the people, you can consciously see the other athletes, you can hear the tannoy, and

Steve Backley. His ability to rehearse a throw in his mind gives him the edge over his competitors. 'In competition, it's like I'm getting an extra throw.'

whatever's being said, what races are on the track. You come in and throw again and again and again, you try the first round, the last round, the middle rounds, you're winning, you're losing, the rain's coming down, the sun's shining, every possible factor that you might have to come up against, whether it be a problem or not a problem, you do it over and over again.

■ The absence of malice in Backley's imaginary Olympic stadium is a revealing aspect to what motivates him. In his vivid description of the javelin event, there are only cursory references to other medal contenders, competitors and opponents. Rivals is too strong a description for him. For the purposes of competition, Backley's javelin throwing world is clinical and impersonal to the extreme. In his discipline, the challenge is the distance, not the individual.

This may be a function of his reluctance to set specific targets, like the championship qualifying distance, the 85 metre mark, the world record. As he has previously explained, to do this would interfere with the mental preparation for maintaining a smooth throwing action. It would spell disaster. If he visualised a winning distance and thought about this on the run up, he could well find the throw over in his head before the javelin had left his grip. Visualise a winning distance and the image might as well involve Backley walking up to the mark and planting the javelin in the ground instead of trying to throw it.

The explosive world of sprinting is not so detached. It is a power event that is beyond athletes without the inner drive to motivate themselves sufficiently. The sprinting machine runs on adrenaline. Backley's adrenaline quota must be carefully balanced to enhance his competitiveness without sacrificing technique. He also seems too nice a guy for the bear pit of athletics, better off imagining the perfect throw in the slightly sanitised world of javelins.

The cut and thrust of the straight 100 metres belongs to others. The 100 metre sprint is *made* for Linford Christie. When they laid out the first straight track in ancient Greece to honour the fastest serf, they might as well have invited Christie along as a consultant to ensure that the event's specifications would give him the best chance of making his mark in the future. It plays on his pride - in himself and in his country - and demands from him that he performs to his best. The nature of the event is the source of Christie's motivation; as close to head to head combat as you can get on the track, with tactics largely irrelevant. The 100 metres is all heart.

It may surprise those who have watched Christie excel at the Olympics and World Championships that he is deeply respectful towards fellow athletes, whatever the vest. His moving television tribute to the late Ron Pickering, dedicating a championship win to the memory of the former television pundit, was a rare glimpse of this other side. In the stadium, Christie is about as detached from the human element of his surroundings as it is possible to be without seeking another venue to run at. His rivalry with former Olympic gold medalist Carl Lewis is well documented - Lewis failed to qualify for the

USA's Olympic sprint team, largely through injury, and subsequently derided Christie as the champion in his absence - but the pair have, on occasion, shared taxis to meets. This pre-race camaraderie ends at the stadium gates. When they are preparing to run, you would imagine Lewis had diddled his co-passenger on the fare. For Christie, the business of the 100 metres is a serious business. ▶

Linford Christie. 'On the track there is nothing anybody can do to help you. Once you're out there you're on your own. You've just got to focus on doing the job.'

Q. How do you prepare yourself mentally for a race?
LINFORD CHRISTIE: I focus on how fast I am going to run, how far I am going to run, and on my own lane. I block everyone out, and totally ignore everything that's going on around me. If you run 100 metres you've got to focus your vision on 101 metres, because you've got to run 100 metres, and run *through* the line rather than *to* the line. On the track there is nothing anyone out there can do to help you. Once you are out there, your coach, your manager, your friends, they can't do any more to help you. You're on your own. It is just you out there so you just got to focus on doing the job.

The "call up" room before going out on the track is somewhere that is really pressurised. Do you cope with that better than the others?

I've got no problem with that. To be honest, I've been doing it for long enough. My opponents are more scared of me, than I am of them, so I ignore what is going on around me. I don't play that psychological game, people who try to psyche you out, stare you in the eyes, I'm not in to that.

How do you avoid it?

I hold my head really high. When I go in there, I'm the boss. That's how you've got to feel, like you are the best person in there, and if anyone needs to try and psyche me out, it shows that they are scared.

■ Adrenaline-wise, Christie can never really have too much of the stuff. Along with champagne, it is the toast of sprint champions. Adrenaline before the race, bubbly afterwards. Christie admits he is scared before a big championship, but uses the fear to enhance his chances of winning by generating adrenaline through it. He is preparing for a battle. He needs to be ready and prepares his mind accordingly.

It was not always the case. Memories of Christie's early career have been swept away by the force of a late twenties flourish which has extended into a remarkable thirties renaissance. His motivation to run has matured, along with the athlete. Age will eventually catch up with his ability to run fast and fulfil his goals, but it is unlikely that his ambitions will be as easily tamed by Father Time. Until the Old Man does calm him down, Linford Christie will not waste time exchanging pleasantries with opponents at the start. ▶

Q. Before you race, you sit in the warm up with your eyes shut. What do you think about?

LINFORD CHRISTIE: I close my eyes and settle myself to try and get some adrenaline in the system. I run through races and picture different things, anything that might make me scared so that I can bring on the adrenaline. I try and picture my opponents' speed.

Do you ever get scared?

I am always scared. You need the adrenaline, and that's the only way it comes on, so you've got to be scared of losing, of your opponent getting one over on you. There is a lot at stake, the Olympic gold, the World and European Championships.

Do you actually *use* that fear?

You've got to be in control at all times, otherwise it's like when you are in a fight and lose your temper; you know you stand more chance of being beaten up. You must always channel everything and keep it inside.

Christie lives for competition. 'You've got to enjoy seeing your opposition down you when you beat them. And even then, you still want to go out and beat them some more.'

Do you understand people who get to races and then just can't bear to run, and bottle out completely?

I don't. I think if that is the case, then they shouldn't be doing it. Training tells you what you've got to do when you go on the track, so if you get there and then bottle out, that means you are not really cut out to be an athlete.

Have you ever felt like that?

I've *never* ever felt like that. I've always enjoyed racing and that's the reason why I train. I train to go out there and race and to prove that I am the best. It's like a soldier, you are going to war, and there is a chance that you'll be shot at, and so you have got to expect to shoot at people. It's the same for everybody, and if you are out there and you are bottling it, or you are getting scared, that means your opposition is getting scared too, they are just as scared of you as you are of them.

When you were younger, you didn't take it quite as seriously. When did it become what you wanted to do?

The bigger the race you win, the more you feel. Winning feels different as you grow older. When you are eight years old and you win a race, its just a race. Then, when you are 18, you win a race, it feels so much better, because the competition is tougher. The older you get, the bigger the championships, and, obviously the better the feeling.

■ For a man so motivated and determined, so focused on goals, it is a little sad that he maintains that his finest hour was an anti-climax. Maybe it is possible to dismiss an Olympic gold only after you have won one. Christie's lack of satisfaction after his triumph in Barcelona reveals a man driven by the next challenge, the moment the last one has been accomplished. ▶

Q. Can you describe what it was like to win gold at Barcelona?

LINFORD CHRISTIE: To me it was one big anti-climax, because I was expecting to feel this great feeling, and to me it was just another race. I was happy for the people

around me, my coach, my friends, my supporters and sponsors as they put a lot in, but, for myself, it didn't really feel that great at all.

What makes you carry on?
I suppose it's my expectation.

Not the winning?
I enjoy the adrenaline flow, I enjoy the competition, I enjoy meeting people and I enjoy showing the world how good I am. Beating Carol Lewis at Gateshead (after Lewis had missed the 1992 Olympic 100 metres) gave me the greatest thrill so far because he had a big mouth. He wasn't in the Olympic games and they tried to take away from me a lot of what I had achieved. The media gave him space in the papers to have a dig at me.

How did you feel about Gateshead?
It was a better feeling than actually winning at the Olympics. My motto is, "never mouth off your opposition", because it gives them five or ten percent more to go out there and kick your butt with, and that is exactly what happened. Maybe if Lewis had kept quiet the result would have been different, but because of everything, I trained a lot harder, and I was able to beat him, so it was a much better feeling. He came into my territory and then he had to eat humble pie. I didn't say anything to the media. I just kept quiet, and let my feet do the talking.

What does it take to be a champion?
More than anything else, you have always got to believe you are the best, that there is nobody out there better than you. If you lose your way, you have got to believe that you will make a comeback, you should never accept second place, and you should never believe that it is *not* the winning, it's the taking part, because it is always the winning. Nobody remembers the people who take part, they remember the winners. You should also never believe that you know too much because you can always learn, even from people who are not as good as you. You have got to believe that, no matter how many years you have been in the sport, any kind of sport, there is something more you can learn. Once you can accept that then you are on your way to being a champion.

Do you particularly want recognition from the general public, your peers or anyone else?
You want people out there to know that you are doing something worthwhile. You've got to go out there and earn the respect. It is hard work, you've got to put up with a lot but that's where the fighting spirit comes, and you've got to fight through all that, you can't worry what people think about you at the end of the day. Obviously everybody wants to be liked or whatever, but for every one person that likes you there are always two who don't.

■ The motivation of this rage is definitely something for the psychologists to consider. Chrisite on the couch would present most of them with a challenge equal to the one Christie presents to his opponents on the track. They would find the easy-going individual happy to indulge their questions a very different beast to the track carnivore that wins gold after gold.

They may worry about Christie. His motivation has a negative side to it - the fear of failure is certainly part of it. It is far removed from the "competing, not the winning" philosophy that the Olympic movement is founded on. For Christie, who has been seen celebrating the pure spirit of competition during the informalities of many a closing ceremony, medals matter more.

It doesn't always have to be this way. Sometimes motivation is as straight forward as the colour of an athlete's vest. As well as records and medals, Graeme Obree craves a chance to cycle for his country, Scotland, at a major championship. He even contemplated

Dos and Don'ts Before a Race

"Do Not wear anything for the first time - spikes or shorts or anything - in a race. If your shorts are sewn wrongly and you are running 5000m you can be in serious pain after 3000m."
Martin Steele (800m runner)

"Do Not have any doubts in yourself."
Zita Lusack (Gymnast)

"Do whatever feels good for you - don't do things just because you're told to."
Linford Christie (100m sprinter)

THE MAIN CONTENDERS

YVONNE MURRAY
Date of Birth: 14 April 1964
Height: 5' 8" / 1.73 m
Weight: 8st / 51 kg

COMPETITION RECORD:
3000m: 1993 World Indoor champion;
1990 European champion;
1990 Commonwealth silver;
1989 World Cup champion;
1988 Olympic bronze;
1987 European Indoor champion;
1986 European Indoor silver;
1985 European Indoor bronze.

1500m: 1993 European Cup bronze.

FEARS AND SUPERSTITIONS

Competition is a stressful time for most athletes. It's probably not surprising that a large number of athletes are superstitious. They might have a lucky charm, or an omen of good or bad luck, or an intricate ritual that they have to go through before a race. Everything from fear of cemetaries, to lucky earrings and reading car magazines the night before a big meet.

LUCKY CHARMS

"I have two large gold earrings. I don't know why they're lucky, but I wore them for the UK champs last year, and that's where I sort of made my name, so I wear them all the time now." Kelly Holmes (800m runner)

"My lucky watch, the watch I broke the world record with, and won the world championships with, so I can't leave home without it." Colin Jackson (110m hurdler)

"I don't have anything that is a lucky charm, I think sometimes that can work against you, if you forget it or something like that ... I used to wear the same pair of shorts, same pair of socks all the time, but after a while mum flung them out". Yvonne Murray (3000m runner)

"I have a horseshoe. My cousin had good luck printed over it as a lucky charm. I don't carry it to every event, but to the important ones, and the ones that will make a difference." Nick Gillingham (200m breaststroke)

"No, never have one, in case you leave it behind" Linford Christie (100m sprinter)

SUPERSTITIONS

"I never cut my nails during a competition - it might bring bad luck." Gill Clark (badminton player)

Linford Christie sees himself as mentally stronger than any other track athlete in the world. He would never carry a lucky charm — his confidence comes from within.

SEX BEFORE THE RACES?

If there is one question most sports people would like science to answer, it's how far to take their dedication to sport into the night before the big event.

"No, not for three days before a race. People say that it's okay for women, but men tire themselves out. I don't know if there's any truth in it, but I don't want to take the risk. But the night *after* a race...."
Linford Christie (100m sprinter)

"No problem at all."
Martin Steele (800m runner)

"They say it does relax you a little bit, but I have my own routine, and I'm not going to divulge it."
Yvonne Murray (3000m runner)

"Sex before a race is no problem at all... So long as it doesn't make you late for the start." Graeme Obree (cyclist)

The medical view...
"Male athletes achieve better results after a week of abstinence, while female athletes achieve better results when having sexual activity during the week prior to the contest. The difference is significant, particularly for power/strength based sports. For sports that need improvisation the results are quite different."
Dr Mordechai Halperin, Jerusalem Medical Centre for Impotence and Infertility

"Our studies showed that sex with orgasm maximises the quality of sleep for men and women. That can have a very beneficial effect on pre-competition tension, and there are no detrimental physical effects."
Dr Craig Sharp, University of Limerick

accepting an invitation to compete on behalf of his fellow Scots in the 1994 Commonwealth Games (the highest level where the Union's constituent parts compete separately) even though it clashes with the professional World Championships. The thistle is an inspiring symbol.

There is something very endearing about this outlook - more so than Christie's, who although no less patriotic, somehow seems too angry with himself for such sentiments. Obree reflects: "It would be wonderful to go to the Commonwealth Games for of a chance to run out under the Scottish flag. It would be as potentially satisfying to me as winning the World Championships. Once you get to the World's you are talking "God Save the Queen" and everything, which is all very nice but, not getting political, the Commonwealth Games is the highest level for the Scottish people.

Obree has missed the opportunities to ride for Scotland in previous Commonwealth Games. His motivation to compete echoes the words of another of his countrymen, Robert the Bruce, who urged: "If at first you don't succeed, try, try, try again." After the experiences of Matt Yates, it is quite refreshing to find an achiever whose drive to compete is no more complex than plain national pride.

FILMING BADMINTON

If anybody had asked me at the outset of the filming of this series what was going to be the hardest thing to capture, I would not have said badminton. As it turned out, I have never had a tougher task than trying to convey the speed and incredible voracity of a game between England's top mixed doubles pairings Nick Ponting and Joe Wright, and Chris Hunt and Jill Clark. When you watch a game of badminton it seems very clear where the action is at any one time. Our eyes and brains are excellent at following the pace of play and piecing the action together. Only when you view the game through a camera lens and try to follow that action do you realise just how clever our eyes and brains are! In competition badminton the shuttle cock is frequently travelling faster than 100 miles an hour, and in a dimly-lit sports hall the finest cameramen would find it impossible to follow. The only way we could think of giving ourselves a chance of conveying the incredible speed and agility of the game was to plan and stage a completely controllable rally and then to film each shot of that rally separately from several angles. Nick, Joy, Chris and Gill gamely volunteered themselves for what was to be a long and tricky day's filming. We lit only one side of the badminton court and filmed each shot one after the other from the same side of the court. This enabled us to put a scaffolding tower directly in the centre of the receiving court to act as a camera platform from which to get high angle shots of the players making their strokes. Whilst the effect

Far from the gentle game that many perceive it to be, badminton is a furiously paced sport. We consider stopping the shuttlecock in mid-flight a major achievement.

Filming Badminton

that the edited film would produce was of a continuous rally of six shots, during the filming the shuttlecock was never hit more than once at a time.

Even so, actually capturing the shuttlecock in frame was virtually impossible. Though the film when processed would run in slow motion, through the camera viewfinder things still happen in real time. It is impossible to judge whether what you have seen through it is a close up of a shuttle cock hitting the strings of a badminton racket, or just a swish of badminton racket: everything is over in less than one hundredth of a second. We hoped to get around this by having the shuttlecock travel directly towards the camera. This would mean that instead of passing through the frame from side-to-side, at least it should be in there for long enough to be seen! But getting the shuttlecock to travel along that line is harder than it might sound. The best way to do it, we decided, was to use a piece of elastic and some cotton attached to the shuttlecock and to fling it directly at the camera lens. We were mid-way through setting this up when Nick Ponting had a better idea: 'Why not', he said 'let me just smash the shuttle cock from one side of the court directly at the camera on the other.' He was sure he could get pretty close. Rather sceptically I said that he would never, over a distance of 25 feet, get anywhere near a lens less than 3 inches in diameter. But he insisted on having a go and for the sake of argument we let him try.

Out of around 10 shots, more than half hit the camera lens and the rest missed by only one or two inches. It was a fantastic film sequence. Nick - I'm sorry I doubted you... R.D.

Filming Shirley Macintosh

Standing beneath the low vaulted ceiling of Edinburgh University's rifle range watching Shirley Mackintosh shoot, the one thing that strikes you most is the silence. When we decided to film Shirley we knew we needed to capture that quiet concentration. As much as possible we wanted to isolate her in time and space, bathing her in a pool of light within the rifle range.

Adrian, our lighting cameraman, worked hard, fighting against the white reflecting walls to keep the light levels low enough to separate Shirley from the background. The shots we chose were long, static and deliberate: simple shots that allowed the movements Shirley was making to speak for themselves.

The only trick shot we tried was one that Alfred Hitchcock had used in his film "Vertigo". The camera was behind Shirley's head, looking down her line of fire to the distant target. As she took aim the camera tracked backwards on rails and zoomed in at the same time. The effect was to keep Shirley's head and shoulders the same size in the foreground, but to change the perspective of the room she was in: closing in from a wide shot to a single target focused under her gun sights. In "Vertigo", Hitchcock had used the rapidly changing perspective to simulate falling but we hoped it would illustrate perfectly the concentration required to ignore everything else in the room and hit a bulls-eye 10.4 mm wide and 50m away. R.D.

CHARIOTS OF FIRE

"In sport there is a direct correlation between money In and medals Out."

Rob de Castella, Australian Institute of Sport

C hariots of Fire is a great film. A tremendous story. Two outstanding athletes whose experiences on and off the track leading up to the 1924 Paris Olympics provide convenient metaphors for life: Harold Abrahams, driven to win sprint gold by an inner rage fuelled by the Establishment's rejection of him; Eric Liddell, the Scot, a devout Christian, who faced a moral dilemma over whether to run on a Sunday, also shunned for remaining faithful to his convictions. True contenders. Stirring stuff.

In reality, the passage of time and fading memories allowed the film makers to take a few liberties with the truth. Liddell is portrayed as agonising over the sanctity of the Lord's Day on the boat across the Channel en route to the games. In fact, he knew months in advance that the heats of his event, the 100 yard dash, were on a Sunday. His successful switch to the "440" involved little brinkmanship. Other parts have also been enhanced. One of the best moments of the movie features a change in personnel. The American sprinter, Jackson Scholz, delivers a message borrowed from the Bible to Liddell as he warms up on the track for his Olympic final - "those who honour me, I will honour" - before he goes on to triumph. Great moment, but wrong messenger. Great movie, but no documentary.

The sporting public doesn't mind a bit: we constantly seek to enhance accomplishments and play down some of the mundane reality that goes with them. With athletics, this usually involves ignoring the hard work. The image of the amateur is honoured without reference to the hours of preparation even the most gifted athlete has to endure. Corinthians, you see don't take time off work. This attitude infuriated

Harold Abrahams who, in the film, vents his anger against a system that disapproved of him employing a professional coach in his pursuit of an Olympic medal. In respect to the reality of the events, this clip is unerringly accurate in highlighting British athletics' preference, at the time, for the ways of the amateur. Win by all means, Abrahams was told, but make sure no one sees that you are trying, or worse, that you are spending money improving your performance.

That was more than 50 years ago. In many ways little has changed in Britain. A professional approach is merely tolerated by the majority, and embraced fully only by the athletes who have to make sacrifices to continue chasing the dreams of Liddell and Abrahams. Potential Olympians struggle to compete internationally with rivals who benefit from generous state funding and sponsorship from a private sector anxious to assist. Individuals often have to hold down day jobs to finance night work at the track. Many in British athletics are really moonlighting. Linford Christie believes you cannot hold down a full time job and also aspire to being Olympic champion. His own gold medals add weight to this view.

It took a disappointing Olympics at Montreal in 1976 to prompt Australian athletics to consider whether this dated Corinthian-style approach to the sport, a legacy of the nation's former colonial masters, was still effective in the modern world. Australia has a long and proud tradition of success in track and field and of consistent Olympic

Graeme Obree has proved that an unsponsored amateur can reach the top of his sport. But are his like a dying breed?

achievement. The Melbourne games in 1956 yielded 35 medals. By Montreal, this number was down to five with no golds among them. The nation did not hear its anthem. It was "a devastating performance for Australian culture and pride", according to Rob de Castella, the former world champion and record holder in the marathon. There was a public outcry over the sporting shame of the silence.

The reaction was, amusingly, more British than the Australian approach to athletics itself: they formed a committee. But thereafter, Australia departed from the mother country's usual course of action; she did something about the committee's findings. The state enquiry into the organisation of athletics in a country rich in natural talent concluded that the indigenous potential was not being exploited. From this conclusion emerged a plan to establish a centralised institute for sport. In less than five years - itself possibly a world record - the Australian Institute of Sport was founded. The bulk of the country's financial support for athletics is now channelled through this body, a centre of excellence and home for expertise in sports science, coaching, medical research and a large number of potential world beaters.

After 13 years of development and progress, the AIS has, by 1994, grown into a body responsible for around 100 million dollars worth of equipment and facilities devoted to the cause of Australian sport. About 12 to 14 $(AUS) million a year is spent upgrading the existing structure as well as helping new disciplines, in addition to the 20 or so that the AIS has been able to involve itself with during its short life already. The results have encouraged this expansion. In Barcelona, Australia won 27 medals, a figure that suggests she is returning to levels of success enjoyed in the 1950s and 1960s. Harold Abrahams would have been impressed.

The statistics suggest that athletics in the 1990s is as much about money as it is about natural talent. The correlation between money spent on athletics in Australia and medals won in international competition is pretty conclusive. De Castella, now retired from the track and director of the AIS, makes repeated pleas for the funding levels to be maintained so that he, in turn, can deliver the results that a nation mad on sports demanded after Montreal and continues to expect. It is an approach that reflects the modern world of athletics, the "business" of track and field. Passion is no longer enough. Abrahams was 40 years ahead of his time. ▶

Q. How does the Australian Institute of Sport aim to produce athletes of Olympic standard?
ROB DE CASTELLA: By applying a modern Management Approach to the business of sport.

Is that new?
It's new for Australia. Back in the early days, Australia dominated in a lot of sports partly because of our environment, partly because we don't have horrible winters (athletes can get out and train 365 days of the year) and partly because we have a good sporting

Rob Castella, former World Champion marathon runner, now heads the Australian Institute of Sport. 'Its job is to apply modern management techniques to the business of sport.'

culture. We are a strong and healthy nation. Australia was able to come up with more than its fair share of sporting champions, back through the 1950s and the 1960s. But in the 1970s and 1980s, the international environment of sport changed and Australia didn't change. We were still trying to compete in the international arena using attitudes and techniques and structures in place through the 1950s and the 1960s. And we were losing. We reached a low point at the Montreal Olympics in 1976. After that we realised that we had better change.

How vital is the Australian Institute of Sport?
You can't be successful these days in international sport without having a professional attitude. Maybe, every now and then, you get someone who stands apart and can make it to the top, but you know, by and large, you can't do it in a structured and regular and systematic way unless you have a professional attitude. Sport's changed. International sport is a business. There are millions and millions of dollars tied up in the media and the entertainment rights of sport, and that means everyone involved in the high performance sporting industry, has to be very professional in the way they deal with everything.

Have you adopted the approach of the old Eastern European bloc?
We've learnt a lot from the Eastern European approach to their sporting programmes. People look at the old East Germany and say, "That's a horrible way to approach success," but the reality is that sport is an industry. Germany has been very successful in putting in place the necessary structures and programmes to bring about success. They treated sport like a business and they got into the business of sport before everybody else in the world. They also put in place the programmes and the necessary structured approach. What we in Australia did was to take a lot of that philosophy and the approach that the Germans had and apply it to our sporting culture in Australia.

How important is money to this system?
You can't do it without money. It would be nice to think that you could do it just through having the right vision and having the right strategy and structure, the right enthusiasm, but money is vital to put in place the hardware.

Megan Still. In 1989, age sixteen, she had never rowed in her life. Identified by the AIS as a physically suitable candidate for their program, within three years she was competing in an Olympic final.

Is there a correlation between the money put in and international success?
There is no doubt that there is almost a direct correlation between the amount of money that goes into programmes such as the AIS and the results that come out of it. You've got to have the right programmes, structures and systems in place, but if you don't have the money you can't put them in place and still expect to get results. There was a substantial increase in government funding back in 1989. It was a four-year commitment and part of that commitment was to conduct an evaluation and review into the funding which was given to see where it was getting the results. That review was completed in 1993 and it showed quite categorically that there is a substantial increase in both performance and participation as a result of the increased commitment by the government to our sports programmes. In some sports, there was actually a decrease in the financial commitment because there were some events or areas within sports that they wanted to concentrate on, for example, the Australian gymnastics federation decided that it wanted to concentrate on its women's programme at the expense of their men's programme and it reduced the amount of money going to the men. Subsequently there has been a decrease in the sporting results achieved by the men's gymnastics programme and a substantial increase in the results achieved by the women.

How important is science and the pursuit of training techniques, and knowledge about the way the body works, to the system and to the work?
I think science is very important. It is a tool for the coach, and a tool for the athlete to use, and it can answer some of the questions that they have and minimise some of the risks, and take some of the gambling out of sport. The science has to be very specific. We found that the best results from our science programmes are when we have physiologists or scientists who specialise with individual sports. In the early days, we didn't have the resources to be able to dedicate staff to individual sports. The science staff had to reach all of the sports. They could do the routine and the basic testing and provide a little bit of advice on things like weight and skin folds and a few basic measurements, but it's only in recent years where we've been able to expand our science programme and dedicate staff to individual disciplines that they've been able to make some substantial contributions to the programmes. Science is part of the culture, it sets a tone. With the old attitude of just going out and going through the motions and doing it, it doesn't happen. If you do it, you've got to do it well, to get results. You've got to develop the attitude and the science is part of doing that. It's part of the sophistication of Australian sport.

Is it a questioning approach?
You have to have a very inquiring mind. The environment has to be at the cutting edge, forging new ground. Our coaches must sit on the edge of their chairs. We don't want them feeling comfortable. A lot of things will fail, but hopefully we don't waste a lot of

resources. We can pick up the failures early on and concentrate our resources into the one or two successes that we've made.

Can one sport learn anything from another?
One of the great strengths of the Institute is the ability of our coaches to function well together. There's a lot of cross-fertilisation between the different sports. We have over 70 full-time coaches. They are based all around Australia but they're all part of the Institute programme and there is a tremendous amount of communication - an opportunity for the rowing coaches to learn from the basketball coaches and the cricket coaches to learn from the rugby coaches and the track and field coaches to learn from the swimming coaches. We organise a lot of seminars and workshops to ensure that the coaches do have the opportunity to pursue aspects of strength and conditioning training which are applicable to a whole number of sports. There has to be a synergy in place so that the coaches can feed off each other, and come up with new ideas and new ways of doing things. It is an important ingredient. When you're talking about fractions of per cents making the difference between success and failure, winning and losing, then you have to pursue every avenue. We have to challenge the coaches and the coached have to challenge themselves. It means that we have to have different sports feeding off other sports, and putting in place programmes to achieve results.

■ On its own, money is no guarantee of medals. It can be wasted on the wrong athlete. To maximise the yield, the AIS seeks out the raw talent that ultimately is the limiting factor in any nation's accomplishments, be they on the track or in the field. The outstandingly gifted natural will probably always emerge to achieve national and international recognition, but it is debatable whether such a competitor will always maximise his or her potential. The proactive AIS endeavours to leave nothing to chance in this respect and rigorously seeks out talented individuals who possess attributes that should help in achieving success in particular events.

At the beginning of 1994, the AIS had more than 500 individuals each receiving between 4000 and 25,000 $(AUS) a year to assist them in their pursuit of international

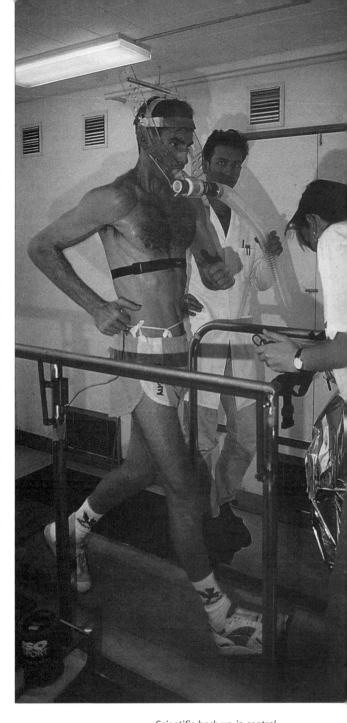

Scientific back-up is central to the Australian programme. 'It can minimise the risks and take some of the gambling out of sport,' says Castella.

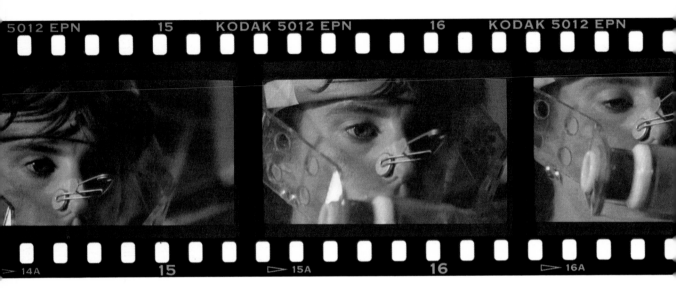

recognition in athletics. They had all been identified early on by the institute as individuals with as yet largely untapped inherent athletic talent. The AIS married them to events that their physical and mental strengths were most suited to, events in which they were most likely to win medals in Olympic, World and Commonwealth championship competition. The results, to date, have been deeply impressive. Take Megan Still. In 1989, aged 16, she had never rowed in her life. After she completed a number of strength endurance tests at schools, the AIS identified her as a physical specimen with innate athletic potential. She was invited to join the rowing programme. Within three years, Still was an Olympic finalist in the coxless women's fours. By Atlanta 1996 she could be a live medal prospect for Australia. ▶

Megan Still is the most successful example so far of Australia's Talent Identification Programme. They hope to have many more in time for the Sydney Olympics.

Q. Has your talent identification programme been successful?

ROB DE CASTELLA: Talent identification is one of the things which we're going to focus on, especially leading up to Sydney in 2000 and beyond. It's partly driven by the fact that we have very limited resources in Australia. We have a small population - 18 million - and we're geographically very spread out so our actual resources in terms of coaches and facilities are spread out too. We have to make sure that when we target someone, when we identify someone, the odds are in our favour to the greatest extent possible, and we're not going to waste those resources on someone who doesn't have the characteristics or the attitude to be successful. That's really what talent identification is primarily about; minimising the losses and the "no wins". It's also about trying to expose athletes and everybody in the community to the most applicable and the most suitable activity in sport for them. We've also a programme called Sports Search. It's a programme which is developed by our "sport for kids" area. It's a software package that goes out to schools, mainly the 13 to 16 year old age group, and it puts the children through a range of different activities and tests and provides a list of the most applicable and suitable sports and activities for a child to pursue. It's developed to ensure that the kids get the most satisfaction and enjoyment out of what they do.

Pairing individuals and events aims to achieve one end: medals. The number Australia wins at future Olympics will be what the AIS is judged on. The equation is a simple one for Castella to calculate and requires him to assess each Olympic discipline with the keen eye of an accountant. From a resources point of view, there are cheap medals and expensive medals. Broadly speaking, team medals are expensive while individual disciplines are better value. Of course, some medals attract greater public kudos and are therefore worth devoting extra resources to than ones awarded for lower profile competition. A gold in the 1500 metres would certainly be worth its weight to Castella. But overall it's a numbers game. Sydney's success in winning the right to host the millennium Olympic Games in 2000 has further focused this audit, and challenged the AIS to produce a home team capable of bagging 60 medals. Bearing in mind the expansion of the games since 1956, the figure compares with the yield from the last Australian Games in neighbouring Melbourne. If it is achieved, Australia will have come full circle.

'The facilities there are fantastic. It's just amazing to be in that sort of environment where everybody is there for you and everyone wants to help you.'

British athletics has not benefited from the attention that a home Olympics brings since 1908. Nevertheless there have been plenty of talented individuals and great Olympic moments since then. The national anthem has been heard just about often enough to satisfy a deeply critical home audience which has high expectations of its sportsmen and women when they perform on the world stage. There has been no public outcry to match the volume of the Australian protest after Montreal.

This is a tribute to the individual. There is no AIS equivalent in Britain. Future stars begin competing in school and club athletics and then advance to representative level and hopefully honours. For the most successful, sponsors ultimately provide the financial cushion that enables the talented to concentrate on developing techniques and skills on the training ground. Although some support is forthcoming from the state, it is modest fare compared with the handouts the equally gifted receive in Australia. There, raw potential benefits from the enforced *largesse* of the tax payer. In Britain, the individual must produce the goods first before being considered. This must be done without much help, centralised or otherwise.

It is a system that has produced many good - and some great - athletes. What alarms those directly involved in ensuring Britain wins her share of golds is the number of potential medal winners who never see the light of day. There is little organised talent spotting, other than that which local clubs do to vicariously enhance their reputations through the achievement of their members. If an athlete emerges, it is not a consequence of a particularly efficient talent spotting system. There is an unhealthy slice of luck involved.

Flaws such as this exist throughout the system. Even when talent does emerge through good fortune, little effort is made to nurture it. Kelly Holmes is a good example. She won three 1500 metre English schools titles up to 1987 and was one of Britain's most promising athletes at that stage. A year later she joined the army. In doing so, she was effectively retired from competitive athletics.

The army was oblivious to her talents. Only unsuspecting new recruits were exposed to the latent gifts of Corporal Holmes. She would challenge self-confident newcomers on their first army run to a race back to barracks. The young men would snigger and be run into the ground. Even when, galvanised by the spectacle of a women's middle distance Olympic final in Barcelona without British interest, she resumed training, the Army was unimpressed that by the end of 1993 she was the fifth best British women's 800 metre runner of all time. The Army rewarded her achievements by insisting that she carried out normal duties. Athletics administrators were equally indifferent. She admits it was partly her fault as she "never makes a fuss", but now, with her abilities belatedly acknowledged, she hopes to honour her regiment and country on the track, even if they have been slow to honour her.

Australia's 'Sports Search' programme aims to assess every schoolchild in the country for their athletic potential.

For others, it can be worse. In some respects, Kelly Holmes is lucky. Although she suffered in the struggle for attention by being a woman in the Army, she was, at least, competing in a high profile event. This increases the likelihood of her receiving at least some funding and support to help with training. For British athletes in disciplines that receive only limited limelight, compared with glamour events like Linford Christie's 100 metres, it is even harder to get recognition and consequently, help.

Sometimes this means British athletics loses a gifted performer. Kerry Shacklock is one half of the UK synchronised swimming duet champions (Laila Vakil is the other). Doing a television advert helped finance her training, but it is unlikely to provide for a career of international competition and she may have to quit. For others the problems run deeper. Money alone is not enough. There is nothing to spend it on in Britain. Some athletes like Debbie Southwick, Britain's premier rhythmic gymnast, find themselves having to go abroad to find adequate training centres and the specialist technical coaching they need to fulfil potential that could be converted into medals at Commonwealth Games level or higher. Compared to the AIS, Britain fails to nurture its

Australian experience proves that money spent is directly proportional to medals won.

talents, funds them belatedly, and if it does, inadequate facilities drive them abroad. The amateur spirit is alive and well.

For Southwick, Russia was the only option. Having mopped up domestic honours with veritable ease, she had to look to Eastern Bloc countries like Russia and Bulgaria, where rhythmic gymnasts are household names, for tutors to take her to the next level in the event. She would much rather have stayed at home.

Q. Were you talent spotted?
DEBBIE SOUTHWICK: Britain had never had a rhythmic gymnast like me before. I came around just as rhythmic gymnastics was changing. A new code for the sport had just been introduced and it was as if it was written for me. There was nobody in Britain and then I came along from nowhere. They grabbed me.

How did you discover that you couldn't be coached in Britain?
It wasn't anything to do with me, it was the coaches in charge in Britain. They said "Debbie needs special training, she can't do it here, we don't have the facilities or the coaching skills to do it here. Debbie's going to have to go abroad". That was it. It wasn't like I had a choice in it. You've got to go abroad if you want to be a good gymnast. They had a Russian contact and they brought this coach over. First of all it wasn't going to be us going to Moscow, it was going to be her coming to Britain and then she said, "no,

Debbie's got to come to Moscow if she wants to get the best training possible". I'd go for two weeks and then it just dragged on and on. Before I knew it I was living there. It was really difficult because at first it had always been really short term, and then suddenly Moscow was my home and that was really hard.

In other sports they can train everybody to top levels in Britain, but they had to send you abroad. How do you feel about that?
It is so tough for someone to understand what it's like to train. It's not like going to train in France or going to train in Switzerland, you're going to train in Moscow and Bulgaria and they're not the nicest of places to live. They're so far behind us, about 20, 30 years, and they don't have all we have. It's really annoying that they have to be the best. Why can't America be the best at it and we can go and train there?

Would you like to have been able to train in Britain?
I would have loved to. It's not that we don't have the coaches, it's just that we don't have facilities or the money to be able to set up a gymnastics school. In Britain, there is nowhere in the country that's purpose built for rhythmic gymnastics.

Australia seeks out and nurtures its young talent. Should Britain be doing more?

■ So much for England's green and pleasant land. Without a body like the AIS and the support it provides, the likes of Holmes, Shacklock, and Southwick have to have real

desire to perserver with their efforts to emulate Linford Christie.

They still have it all to prove. In contrast, Christie has done it all. As Olympic and world champion he has been successful enough to take advantage of more relaxed rules that govern the financial rewards athletes are now allowed to claim. He is comfortably a millionaire, from endorsements and direct earnings from competing. Unlike the struggling trio, he does not have to worry about money. He trains where the conditions are most likely to enhance his performance - not Russia - existing within of a "virtuous circle", where success funds success.

Christie is not without compassion, but he thinks it is, broadly speaking, as it should be. He believes he has

THE MAIN CONTENDERS

STEVE BACKLEY
Date of Birth: 12 February 1969
Height: 6' 4" / 1.93 m
Weight: 14st 13lbs / 95 kg

COMPETITION RECORD:
Javelin: 1993 World Championships 4th;
1992 Olympic bronze;
1991, 1989 World Student Games champion;
1990 European champion;
1990 Commonwealth champion;
1989 European Cup champion;
1989 World Cup champion.

Australia's impressive bio-mechanics lab in Canberra (opposite) stands in stark contrast to West London's stadium that has been re-named to honour the fastest man in the world, who trains there. Proof that facilities alone are not enough?

earned his rewards, that they reflect his talents. He also maintains that he would not have achieved what he has if he had been cosseted within a structure like the AIS. His motivation has always been based on hunger. He believes that young athletes do not benefit greatly from having everything provided for them. It makes them soft. If Linford Christie was a headmaster, it would be of the School of Hard Knocks. His students would go on to graduate from the athletics equivalent of the University of Life before climbing the winner's rostrum.

This does not mean that Britain's premier athlete believes that the sport he has graced with such distinction is over-funded. On the contrary. Indeed, Christie has got plenty to say on the British government's attitude towards state support for athletics. It's just that his own experience suggests to him that young athletes who are provided with everything on an AIS plate have no edge. They have no desire. His point is that athletes who have it all at an early stage in their careers do not want more later on. The right to some of the limited funds the various sporting associations and bodies have at their disposal for the benefit of national athletes should be earned.

When it comes to a young athlete whom he feels is deserving like Darren Campbell, Christie is generous, both with his time and with his money. Campbell is an unusually talented athlete, with the potential to compete at the highest level. Christie recognised this - as well as seeing something of himself as a young man in Campbell - and afforded him limited financial help as well as allowing him to accompany him and Colin Jackson to their winter, warm weather training venue. This is, ironically, Australia, but his

preference for the country that leads the world in establishing a structure to unearth and develop new athletic talent, does not dilute his conviction. Nor does his support of Campbell. He firmly believes that humble origins make for the best champions. ▶

Q. Does Britain do enough for talented young athletes?

LINFORD CHRISTIE: I honestly believe that, as a country, we should be doing more. I think the government is not doing enough. They jump on the bandwagon when we achieve. They shouldn't because they put very little in. They tax the money that's raised to send athletes like myself to the Olympic Games. We must be the only country in the world that does things like that, and the country as a whole does not encourage winners. When you're up and coming you need encouragement, you need to be able to concentrate.

Darren Campbell says you're very generous.

It's nice of Darren to say I'm very generous. I don't think I'm materialistic at all. You can't take it all with you but maybe it can be an investment. If I can invest a little bit in talents like Darren then eventually, if he makes it, he in turn can invest a little bit in the next person that comes along. I'm not looking for a repayment or anything, I just think that someone helped me and I, in turn, can help somebody.

Do you think it's your job to be able to help Darren?

No, not really, but, the way things are, if you rely on other people then it may not happen.

Seen in the UK as very much the 'poor relation', Rhythmic Gymnastics receives little support compared to Artistic Gymnastics. Debbie Southwick sacrificed her childhood to find coaching in the Eastern Bloc.

THE MAIN CONTENDERS

ROBERT MORGAN
Date of Birth: 27 March 1967
Height: 5' 10" / 1.78 m
Weight: 11st 9lbs / 74 kg

COMPETITION RECORD:
Highboard Diving: 1993 European
Championship silver; 1992 Olympic Games
5th; 1991 European Championship bronze;
1990 Commonwealth champion.
Springboard Diving: 1993 European
Championship 4th.

The best way if you want something done is to do it yourself and that's been my attitude.

Do you think there is a risk of you helping Darren too much?
No, not at all. I believe there's got be an element of struggle somewhere along the line and I think I know exactly how far to go. If you help people too much then some people are ungrateful or they depend on it and I tend not to allow that to happen. I don't want the people that I assist to be dependent on it. They've *got* to struggle because I did, and I think the struggling part of life is good. That's what makes you tough, builds your character.

If athletes have to struggle does it improve their racing?
Definitely. The thing about athletics, it's about wanting. You've got to want it. There's a saying in the Bible, it's easier for a camel to go through the eye of a needle than for a rich man to enter the Kingdom of Heaven. I really do believe that's true in athletics. If you've got it all then you haven't got motivation. You've got to have nothing and want everything. It's all about being ambitious and you can't be *too* ambitious. A lot of people come into the sport because they believe there's easy money in it and they've got the wrong attitude. You've got to come in feeling hungry, desperate and ready to appreciate what you get. That's what it's all about.

Is there enough help for other talented young athletes?
No, not really, there's isn't enough. I think a lot of the money sometimes goes to the wrong people. They say it's human judgement, we've got to rely on other people to think

whether or not this one's got the talent. To be honest with you, I have no faith in that kind of system because I had the talent and none of them would have recognised it or given out grants.

Money takes away a lot of the pressures. People don't have to worry about making ends meet and so on. Do you think all athletes should have some financial support?
Not in the beginning. I think all athletes should go through a period of struggle. In Australia, where they put so many millions of Australian dollars into sport science, you can't see the benefit. From what I can see, the people who are really benefiting from it are the cyclists and the rowers. For me, my coach has the science that makes me work. I haven't had any assistance from a federation or anything like that. A lot of it's just logical thinking to be honest with you. In running, you have to teach your body to go forward. You train your body to do that as fast as possible and that's all you need to know.

What sort of logical thinking?
Take my weight training for instance. I learned the basic weight training from just watching other people and talking to coaches. Then I went away and I started doing my own thing. I decided where I was, and I started developing those things and that's all it was really.

Corporal Kelly Holmes is the fifth fastest British woman 800 metre runner of all time. She may have to sacrifice her sporting career in order to fulfil her commitments to the British Army.

What difference does having money make to your training and your ability to train?
Money makes the world go round. It really does and you can't survive without it.
Personally, it takes my mind off having to struggle. I can get up and say "Okay, I don't
want to train here, it's cold. I want to go abroad and train in the sunshine", and I don't
have to worry about asking people for the money. I can pay my way, pay my coach's way. I
use the money I earn in athletics to make me better in athletics. I re-invest my money
to make me a better athlete and I can go out there and earn twice as much. I just
speculate to accumulate.

■ The approach certainly worked for Linford Christie. Few are as motivated, even today.
The danger, though, is in leaving the future of British athletics to chance. In his School
of Hard Knocks, there is little time spent - Campbell aside - nurturing talent. If it
emerges, it emerges. If it does, it will probably be awesome, like Linford Christie
himself. If, for whatever reason, it doesn't, for "Australia, Montreal 1976" read, "Britain,
Atlanta 1996.........."

It's a high risk strategy: All, or nothing. Others in British athletics are less prepared
to leave the future of many talented youngsters to the athletic equivalent of the free
market. Tommy Boyle has coached Yvonne Murray to many great moments since 1987,
but has become increasingly worried about the future of athletic talent in his beloved
Scotland.

While Australia followed the examples set in the 1970s by the East European
countries, Boyle, compelled by the apathy of administrators has established his own
talent-spotting network. Murray, an inspiration to young Scottish athletes contemplating
a future on the track, assists him in searching out young talent. The pair believe that if
they hadn't acted, the blue vest of Scotland, filled with such distinction by Eric Liddell,
might not do its former wearer justice in the future.

Boyle went to schools in search of future champions. It was a struggle as at least half
the potential talent in the classroom was hooked on playing for Rangers or Celtic.
Undeterred, he organised athletics oriented events to expose children to the disciplines
of the track and field. Since starting in 1991, he had been encouraged by the progress he
and Murray, who is a strong role model for many in Scotland, have made. In early stages
of the venture, many children lured into participating could only manage two laps before
gasping for their Sega Megadrives. Three years on, gadgets lie dormant while the same
children complete a cross country course that had to be extended to provide them with
an adequate challenge. Few hedgehogs, answering to the name Sonic, are found on this
particular scenic and healthy route.

If there is another Yvonne Murray out there, Boyle should find her. And there are
other spin-offs. His motivation is broader than just the search for Olympic glory for his
country. He also aims to address the problems of increases in the incidence of heart
disease, and a decline in standards of diet and level of general exercise that are so
prevalent in some areas of Scotland. He wants a healthy Scotland and has been granted

funding to stage more of these "athletics awareness" gatherings. The aim of improving the general health of the nation is, on its own, sufficient to justify the projects. ▶

Q. What is the aim of the events you stage with Yvonne Murray?
TOMMY BOYLE: We are trying to bring the talent that is in the schools into athletics. Once that talent is channelled towards athletics we will have a more structured approach to their career in the sport. Hopefully we'll produce another Yvonne Murray in about ten years time.

Why do you need to do this to find them?
Because they're no longer participating in sport. We've had to recreate an environment which encourages the kids actually to participate again. We've created our own recruitment programme; Indoor athletics, cross-country, and track and field. Throughout the year, the kids have the opportunity to be exposed to athletics. From each of those recruitment programmes we'll find the most talented kids in the area, give them lots of encouragement, give them a structured programme, and hopefully produce some champions.

What was the alternative?
I realised that athletics was dying as a sport in Scotland. I've been in athletics for 25 years, and coached at the very highest level with Yvonne Murray. I recognised that there would be no future Yvonne Murrays unless somebody did something. And it took somebody who had a bit of stature in the sport - a bit of presence in the local community

Yvonne Murray and coach Tommy Boyle take it upon themselves to encourage Scottish youngsters to take up their sport. 'I realised that there would be no future Yvonne Murrays unless somebody did something.'

- to give everybody a shake and try and pool the resources together. That's exactly what I've tried to do. So what we have actually got is a unique situation where we have top level athletes, top level coaches, the community council, the District council itself, leisure services and lots and lots of volunteers, all working together to the same end.

What is that end?
The end is to get more kids involved in sport. To try and give them an opportunity to exercise in a fun way and hopefully to produce some champions.

Do you feel Britain as a country should have more programmes?
I think if there's to be a future in sports like athletics, then we must be a lot more innovative. We've got to look at what turns kids on today. When I was a youngster we used to run cross country, across ploughed fields. These kids won't do that. Bring them into this type of environment, where it's fun - they're not really inhibited by it - and they'll all join in, and you've got a successful recipe for the future. There are some projects throughout Britain, but what we need to do is get a whole structure of programmes in every district and every council and every borough in the country to fill the gap, and ensure that every child is given the opportunity to participate.

■ The sight of a gym full of children running in all directions is wonderfully removed from the demanding world of modern track and field. There is a healthy element in Boyle's idea of sport as recreation. It keeps sport in perspective. Athletics *should* be fun. The sentiment, particularly in junior athletics, is important.

The AIS is establishing itself as a yardstick for excellence in athletics, a model that other countries would do well to follow. But even gold can be scant compensation for the sacrifices an individual has to make to win it. It is a free world and some are prepared to pay, but even the most determined occasionally stop and think. Debbie Southwick went willingly to Russia to pursue her career in rhythmic gymnastics. After a fortnight she wondered whether it was all worth it. ▶

Debbie Southwick. 'Some mornings when I wake up I just think "Oh why don't I just give up, why don't I just call it a day." '

Q. What was Russian coaching like?
DEBBIE SOUTHWICK: They have a very old system. They think it's the shouting, the screaming, the hitting, and the crying that works. There'd be days in the gym when you could swim in the tears. Every one of us would just be crying. You'd be brought down to a level where you thought you were really bad. I was never praised. If I'd done a routine and it was fine and I felt quite good afterwards, they'd always find faults, never positive things.

That's fair enough, but I always think that you should say something positive after a routine. If it's always negative then it brings the performer down. That's what happened to me. I was brought down so far that I had such a low opinion of myself, and of my gymnastics, that it was really hard in competition to be suddenly all sparkly.

Where you ever hit?
The coaches never used to actually hit us. They'd hit the Russian gymnasts because they could. They are treated like that because the parents of the Russian gymnasts give their permission to the coaches. They never see their daughters, and are often thought to be the responsibility of the coaches.

Why did you stay?
I stayed because of the Olympics really, that was the only thing.

Do you still think about giving up?
I think about it all the time. Some mornings when I wake up I just think "Oh why don't I just call it a day, why am I doing this?" Sometimes, when I'm in the gym and I'm

Despite his world success, Linford Christie still trains with the club runners at the stadium where he grew up. He sees advantages in the School of Hard Knocks.

stretching and my body's really aching from the day before I think, "Why?". Then other times, I'd say it's events like the Commonwealth Games and the Olympics that keep me going.

When you look back, do you have any regrets about the way you've grown up?
Sometimes, I'm quite unhappy about what I've missed out on. I just wish I could have done this and that, but I took five months off because I pulled two ligaments in my foot and in those five months I did things that I'd never done before. I was a normal person as such and I'd eat what I want and I wouldn't go the gym - that was really weird - and it was quite strange. I thought "God, I can get used to this! I'm enjoying this too much, not going to the gym and not training", and it was really hard to kick-start back into a routine.

What made you decide to come back?
I'd had enough of slobbing about basically. I came back off holiday, looked at myself and thought I could really do with getting back into shape and getting fit. I thought "I'm still the best, I know I can do it. I'm going to get fit again and then I'm going to review the situation".

■ The Olympics and Commonwealth Games needed to draw on all their history to win back Debbie Southwick in Russia. They do not need all their pulling power to convince Megan Still. The homely nature of the AIS is very different to the "institution" Debbie Southwick was committed to in the absence of adequate facilities in Britain. Still talks enthusiastically about how much fun life at the AIS is, and de Castella, her director, maintains that the graduates benefit as individuals from their experiences there. They enjoy the camaraderie and healthy competition. Athletes who are accepted by the AIS and fail in their respective events can still go on to challenges in other walks of life, applying the lessons they have learned on the track to reality.

The School of Hard Knocks is less successful in converting losers into rounded personalities. A struggling competitor with the hunger, but not the talent, can retire embittered towards others more gifted at pursuing their goals. Back-markers and contenders alike may also drive themselves to physical harm in such a place: it is unlikely, for instance, that athletes at the AIS would be allowed to over-train themselves to the point of injury, but a sink-or-swim atmosphere would seem ideal encouragement to do just that.

Ultimately, though, the stubbornness of youth prevails. Like horses, you cannot make young athletes drink, and less still, run, jump and throw. You can try - even force them - but you won't produce an Olympic champion, only very bitter and twisted under-achievers. Elements of the AIS approach, maybe a term at the School of Hard Knocks and lots of running for fun with Tommy Boyle can contribute to producing track stars of the future - but only if the individual really wants to be a star.

In drawing metaphors for life from the experiences of Harold Abrahams and Eric

Liddell, Chariots of Fire came to a well balanced conclusion about the motivation to succeed. They both won, but in doing so, the film suggested that neither believed that winning was everything. The message of Chariots of Fire is that accomplishments should be gauged against an individual's potential to achieve; to overcome obstacles, to meet challenges, to recover from set backs, and occasionally, to scale the heights that Linford Christie and Colin Jackson have scaled in winning gold.

For a young Darren Campbell, these two world champions represent a goal. If he is good enough and determined enough he too will become a world champion in his own right and, in his turn, a role model for someone else. If he does, what will be important is that he will have made the most of his gifts, he will have fulfilled his athletic potential, and he will hopefully be fulfilled as a person.

In doing so, he may adopt any number of training regimes. He may jog in an aqua suit, or on a treadmill. He may decide to train in the weights room or just at the track, when Jupiter is in the Seventh House or just when he feels like it. Hopefully, he will not *over* train. He may eat chocolate, a lot of chocolate. He may believe in organic vitamins. He may be inspired by his country's vest and an Olympic crowd. He may lock himself in the lavatory. He may honour his inspirations, Christie and Jackson and the

Colin Jackson and Linford Christie use the benefits of their success to encourage athletes among a new generation of British hopefuls.

achievements of Liddell and Abrahams. On another continent, some other young athlete may do the same. ▶

Q. What difference did training with Christie and Jackson make?
DARREN CAMPBELL: I've been told I've always had the talent but, mentally I don't think I was strong until I actually went out to Australia with Linford and Colin. They wind you up... I think it's almost like breathing confidence into you because they make you feel really good about yourself. If you can handle them, when you get onto the track, you feel like you can handle anybody.

How did you meet Linford?
When I was about 14 I was in a sprint competition and I made the final and came second. The medallists went upstairs and met Linford. After that I saw him around the circuit. He never forgot me and I never forgot him and eventually we just became friends.

'I can't take my money with me,' says Christie, 'but maybe I can invest in young talent, and in turn maybe they can invest in the next generation.'

How would you describe Colin and Linford's role with you?

It's more like a guardian-type role because they tend to protect me a lot. Linford will tell me not to do something. Colin always gives me a lot of advice and is always saying "slow things down". He tends to tell me about the reality of what I'm here to do. He makes me think about a lot of things.

How much of a difference has that made for you?

Being based in Manchester and being the fastest, there was nobody who I could really ask for advice. If I've got any problems now I can go to Colin, phone him up or go round and see him and say "Colin I've got this problem. What should I do?" and nine times out of ten Colin will say, "Well, I experienced that at such and such an age and you know, everything will work out in the end." They also got me into training with weights in Australia, so now I'm definitely a lot, lot stronger than I ever was before. Also I used to have a lot of fears that would affect my performance in one way or another. But now I don't really fear anybody mentally either. It's good to have friends like Colin and Linford. I can't ask for much more really.

Are you learning anything about the mental attitude that goes with being a champion from Linford and Colin?

If you needed help they'd help you, but when it comes down to the track, they are selfish. I think, really, to be a champion you've got to be selfish. I've got a lot of friends who go out but I have to make a lot of sacrifices. I found it difficult to make them initially because I've always put my friends first. Now I've become a lot more selfish and I come first. If I decide I'm going to do something I'm going to do it, I'm not going to worry about what anyone else is doing.

How much has being with them taught you when to be serious and when to play?

I always used to take athletics as a laugh because I think that helps me to relax. I don't want to lose that but I think now, once I get to the track, I have to become more serious, especially in training. If you're not putting the work in on the track or in the weights room then you're not going to get the pay back on the track. There was a situation in the weights room in Australia when I'd been there about a week or so and I was messing about and Colin just said to me: "Either do the weights or get out the weights room. You're not here to mess about" and I think that's really when it hit home that it's time to work. Before I used to laugh and giggle in the weights room but now it's just a straight face and work.

What are your ultimate aims?

Career wise that's a secret. It wouldn't be right to tell you all the things that I want to do. I'll tell you one of them, though. I'd like to be Olympic champion at 200 metres. But I can't tell you the other big one.

Are you looking forward to beating Linford one day?
I'd love to beat him, but only because of the way he winds me up. If he didn't wind me up so much I'd probably let him escape that, but now I've definitely got to beat him before he retires. That would be one of my dreams fulfilled.

Spoken like a true contender.